Electronics

Fundamentals and Everyday Applications

Electronics
Fundamentals and Everyday Applications

David P. Beach
William J. Foraker

Delmar Publishers Inc.®

NOTICE TO THE READER

Delmar staff:

Administrative Editor: Wendy Jones
Project Editor: Judith Boyd Nelson
Production Coordinator: Bruce Sherwin
Design Coordinator: Karen Kunz Kemp
Art Coordinator: Michael J. Nelson

For information, address Delmar Publishers Inc.
2 Computer Drive, West, Box 15-015,
Albany, NY 12212-9985

Printed in the United States of America
Published simultaneously in Canada
by Nelson Canada,
a division of The Thomson Corporation

10 9 8 7 6 5 4 3 2 1

Library of Congress Cataloging-in-Publication Data

Beach, David P.
    Electronics: fundamentals and everyday applications / David P. Beach, William J. Foraker.
        p. cm.
    Includes index.
    ISBN 0-8273-4643-3
    1. Electronics. 2. Electronic circuits. 3. Electronic apparatus and appliances. I. Foraker, William J.
II. Title.
TK7816.B4 1991
621.381-dc20
                                                                    90-23558
                                                                    CIP

To my father and mother,
Frank and Martha Beach
D.P.B.

To my wife and son,
Beth and William
W.J.F.

Contents

Preface — Always Safety

Before we start on the body of this book, the authors would like to briefly cover some basic items about safety for electrical and electronic devices and systems. SAFETY IS A CONSTANT. You can forget what time you are supposed to pick up your wife, husband, or date when you are working on electrical circuits. You can forget your social security number. You can forget your name. You can forget anything, BUT DON'T FORGET SAFETY. Electricity is funny stuff. You can't see it. Some old-timers will tell you that they can smell it, although what they are really smelling is ozone. Everyone can feel it but only the true non-believers feel it on purpose. You can't hear it, except when it's in the form of discharges, like lightning, and by the time you hear it you can't do anything anyway. You can't taste it. The point is that the only way to accurately determine the presence and magnitude of electricity is through the use of correctly operated test equipment.

Electricity can hurt you in several ways. Perhaps the most common encounter with electricity is shock. The results of electric shock can range from a mild tingle to instantaneous death. The variables that determine the severity of a shock are the voltage encountered, the current conducted during the shock, the resistance of your body before and during the shock, and the length of time you are part of the electrical circuit.

The rule of thumb is simple. Never place your body in contact with any electrical circuit unless you are sure of the voltage, the current, and the consequences of contact! This means the circuit should be off and should not be turned on by you or anyone else during your contact with it. The human body *will* conduct electricity. The conductivity, or resistance, of the body is affected by many factors, including dryness of the skin, types of clothing and shoes worn, extent of sobriety, and general physical condition. A typical body resistance is 500 ohms. (This will make more sense after you cover Ohm's law early in the book.) At this resistance, even low voltages and low currents can cause involuntary muscle movement, burns, and heart and lung malfunctions. Voltages as low as 24 volts and currents as low as 150 milliamperes have been documented as the cause of fatalities. Also, many injuries occur when a hand is quickly jerked out of a circuit after being shocked. Often the quick motion results in injury when the hand hits a nearby object. You should never attempt to work on or investigate any electrical circuit unless you have specific training to do so. Many circuits, even very simple ones, have the potential to hurt or kill.

Radiation is another hazard of electrical energy. The high-frequency energy found in radio communications and radar can be harmful and even deadly. This is similar to the energy in a microwave oven; if the power were turned on when your hand was inside, the tissues of your hand would be damaged very quickly. Radiation can also induce voltage into conductors. Sailors aboard ship have been shocked when they came in contact with a metal cable that passed through a radio transmitter beam.

Heat, fire, and explosions are other potential hazards of electricity. Everyone knows that irons are hot, but not everyone knows that a simple commutator motor (the kind found in portable hand tools, electric mixers, blenders, etc.) creates small sparks as it operates. When these sparks enter an explosive environment, like a workshop with sawdust in the air or a garage filled with gasoline fumes, an explosion can result. Also, small motors generate heat when they operate. If you place your hand on the case of a small fan motor, it may be hot enough to burn you.

These electrical hazards are not confined to the workplace. Because our homes also contain many electrical devices, a little safety knowledge is essential. The typical 120-volt and the 220-volt circuits in our homes can be deadly. Be careful using electrical devices in the home and even more careful if you try to work on them. Most home appliances are safe to work on when the power is disconnected but some have the ability to store electricity. Older TV sets, for instance, would store over 10,000 volts in the picture tubes for a long time after they were turned off. Newer sets use higher voltages, up to 24,000 volts, but discharge quickly when they are turned off — if they are working properly. Most of us use extension cords all over the house. These are generally safe when used properly, but can be the source of shock or fire when used incorrectly. Always follow the manufacturer's instructions and safety precautions when using electrical devices at home.

This book is intended to introduce you to the principles and applications of electricity and electronics. It will teach you the concepts behind many electrical devices, and their theories of operation. We can't emphasize enough, however, that this information does not provide you with the training to work on electric or electronic circuits except in lab settings with supervision. Electricity has changed our lives in many ways. Let's make sure those ways are for the better.

1

An Abridged History of Electronics

INTRODUCTION

The purpose of this book, and especially of this chapter, is to provide a basic understanding of electricity and electronics and to give some insight into everyday applications. This first chapter gives a very brief history of electronics by highlighting some of its more important developments.

ELECTRICITY AND EARLY COMMUNICATIONS

Since its discovery, electricity has had a major impact on our lives. Electricity gave us electric lights and the electric motor, and electronics gave us the ability to communicate with each other at new levels of speed and convenience.

Human communication was revolutionized by electricity and electronics. By 1831, Joseph Henry had developed a functional telegraph system which could cause a bell to ring as a result of electricity transmitted through wires over long distances. He also developed an early electric relay, which remains an indispensable component of today's electronics systems.

Samuel Morse refined the design and construction of the telegraph. He also developed a universal code of dots and dashes to be used with his equipment. Later, he invented equipment that would record these dots and dashes onto paper tape for transcription at a later time. The Morse telegraph system using Morse code as its language was in widespread use throughout this country well into the 1900s.

Alexander Bell discovered how to convert sound waves into electrical energy, transmit this energy through wires, and convert it back into sound waves. His patent for the telephone was granted on March 7, 1876, and the proliferation of this relatively simple device changed the world. The next milestone in the development of widespread communications was the elimination of the wires needed for long-distance communication.

Although Guglielmo Marconi is often credited with the invention of the wireless telegraph, he actually improved an earlier unserviceable design. By modifying the transmitter power producer, the antenna system, and the receiver circuits, he developed a working system which made its first successful trans-Atlantic communication on December 12, 1901. Although this system did provide for trans-Atlantic telegraph service, it could not reproduce the voice or music.

On Christmas Eve of 1906, the RCA company provided the first public demonstration of their new high-frequency generator by transmitting the first scheduled broadcasts of voice and music in the United States. This generator was a large mechanical device much like today's automotive alternator, and although it was successful, its useful life was very short because, in 1907, Lee De Forest developed a workable version of the vacuum tube.

ELECTRONICS AND THE VACUUM TUBE

The development of the vacuum tube created a clear dividing line between the fields of electricity and electronics. The vacuum tube was capable of producing the radio frequency signals required for radio communication, but it used no moving parts (Figure 1-1). The vacuum tube was also the first electronic component with the potential to amplify and oscillate. Amplification is the ability to convert a weak or small electrical signal into a stronger or larger signal. Amplification also provides for oscillation — stable, consistent variation between two voltage levels. Amplification in the vacuum tube comes from the fact that a very small signal applied to the input causes a very large difference in the signal at the output.

A major drawback of the vacuum tube is that it uses heat to liberate the electrons needed for operation. Not only does the device give off significant amounts of heat when in operation, but it requires large amounts of electricity to produce the heat. Other drawbacks of the vacuum tube include its relatively large size, its fragile physical construction (housed in a thin glass bulb), its limited lifespan, and the high voltages (hazardous to human life) required for normal operation. Despite these problems, however, the vacuum tube remained the most popular electronic component for over fifty years.

RADIO AND TELEVISION

The popularity of radio was one of the most significant factors in the extremely rapid development of the electronics industry. From the early 1920s, radios could not be produced fast enough to satisfy the demand. This gave rise to the electronics repair industry because these first devices were often not very reliable. When radio sets (as they were called) improved in quality and became more available to the average person, radio became the first mass communication medium. Early radios transmitted and received information using AM, or amplitude modulation, a transmission technique discussed in more detail later. This continues to be a popular system but is prone to interference, or unwanted distortion of the signal.

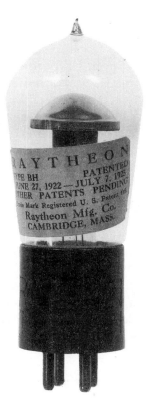

Figure 1-1   An Early Vacuum Tube

For this reason, AM operation is not sufficient for the high-quality commercial applications of today. Instead, FM, or frequency modulation — a different transmission technique — is used because it is much less susceptible to interference and allows the removal of noise from the received signal. It is easy to understand why FM became the medium of choice for music and other high-quality transmissions.

The transmission of sound was not the end of development for communications. People wanted to be able to see all the events that they could then only hear. In 1928, Vladimir Zworykin patented the cathode ray tube, or CRT, as it is abbreviated and often called. This tube emitted electrons just as the vacuum tube did, but, in the CRT, the beam could be steered or directed to hit a target at a specific point. This target was a coated screen which produced light when bombarded with electrons.

The CRT is the television *picture* tube and it has not changed in function or basic design since its invention.

Zworykin not only invented the picture tube, which converts electrical signals into light, but also the *camera* tube, which converts light into electrical signals. These two components were essential to the development of television. Radio and television existed with vacuum tubes very nicely for many years, but the field of electronics has always been on the move. Just over the horizon was the transistor.

SEMICONDUCTORS

In an effort to improve on the vacuum tube, a team of scientists working together at Bell Laboratories from the mid-1940s to the mid-1950s developed what would come to be called the transistor. John Bardeen, Walter Brattain, and William Shockley combined normally nonconducting materials with conducting materials to create a solid material device which became the basis of electronics.

This new device did not need heat to emit electrons. Instead, it accomplished this by taking advantage of some inherent properties of the materials. Size was another advantage of transistors, as they are tiny compared to their vacuum tube counterparts. Transistors were also much more dependable than vacuum tubes and they could process signals considerably faster, although this was not a major concern at the time of their development.

Transistors have had an immense impact on the electronics industry and, because of their size, have given rise to the field of electronic miniaturization. As this field developed, it was found that circuits requiring a relatively large number of components could be combined into a single package. This led to the development of the integrated circuit (IC). The IC is essentially a circuit on a chip, so small that it cannot be directly manipulated by human hands. For this reason the chip is enclosed in a package, which facilitates handling and provides the necessary electrical and physical connections. Today, integrated circuits play a major role in almost all areas of electronics. Their use allows the production of very powerful, efficient, and compact devices.

COMPUTERS

The first totally digital computer, ENIAC, was put into service in 1946. ENIAC could perform 300 multiplications or 5,000 additions per second, but it occupied 1,500 square feet of floor space, weighed 30 tons, and contained over 18,000 vacuum tubes that failed at a rate of about one every 7 minutes. See Figure 1-2 for a general view of the ENIAC. This was obviously not a very workable system. A number of other experimental machines followed until, in 1951, Univac I, the first computer available as a commercial product, was introduced. Univac I was considerably smaller than ENIAC and contained roughly 5,000 vacuum tubes. Forty-eight Univac I computers were built during the early 1950s and many ways to improve their usefulness were devised. In 1953, IBM entered the market with the IBM 701 scientific computer, which became so popular that by the mid-1950s more than 1,000 of them were in use. The 701 was followed by the 702 in 1955 and the more powerful 704 in 1956, which gave IBM a near monopoly on the scientific computer market of the time.

Figure 1-2   General View of the ENIAC (Courtesy of the Moore School of Electrical Engineering, University of Pennsylvania)

After the 1950s, transistors replaced vacuum tubes and computers got faster, smaller, and much more reliable. IBM introduced the 1401 business and the 1620 scientific computers in 1959. During the 1960s, 1970s, and early 1980s, developments in the computer industry proceeded at an extremely rapid rate. The capabilities, size, price, and usability of computers were improved to the point where, today, owning a computer is within reach of the average person. Also, the computer you can buy to sit on your desk has more power than one that would have filled a room only fifteen years ago.

Computers seem complicated and mysterious to people who know little about them. They are actually just very fast and accurate manipulators of two numbers, 1 and 0. Computers are capable of performing calculations at a rate far beyond the capacity of mortals but, alas, they are merely servants. They cannot direct their own activity (yet) and depend on us to give them instructions — called programs and input data. These machines are the topic of several other chapters in this book; their operation and application will be described later in more detail. First, let's find out a little about how electricity works.

2

Basic Theories and Concepts

INTRODUCTION

This chapter covers basic atomic structure, not to make you a physicist, but to allow you to understand something about how electrons move. It also covers voltage, current, and resistance, as they are the bases of all electricity and electronics. Finally, Ohm's law is discussed. It is the primary principle of electronics and will help you understand everything that follows.

ATOMIC CONSTRUCTION

We shall now enter the world of the physicist to determine what electricity is and to learn a little about how it works. In order to understand electricity, it is necessary to know the basic construction of the atom, as the parts of the atom play a major role in electricity.

What is an atom? An atom is the smallest unit of anything that has a distinct set of physical, chemical, and electrical properties. Atoms are the basic building blocks of elements; elements can be combined to form compounds. Compounds make up everything we see, feel, taste, and smell every day. Molecules are clumps of atoms that are either of the same element or of different elements. If a molecule is made of atoms of the same element, it has the same properties as the individual atoms, thus the same as those of the element. If a molecule is made up of atoms from different elements, it can, and probably does, take on a new set of properties.

Consider the following example. Wood is a compound. It is made up of several elements arranged in specific combinations. Two of the elements in wood are carbon and hydrogen. Thus, carbon and hydrogen atoms are arranged with other atoms to make up wood molecules. Many wood molecules make up a baseball bat. If this concept is not clear yet, perhaps an analogy would help.

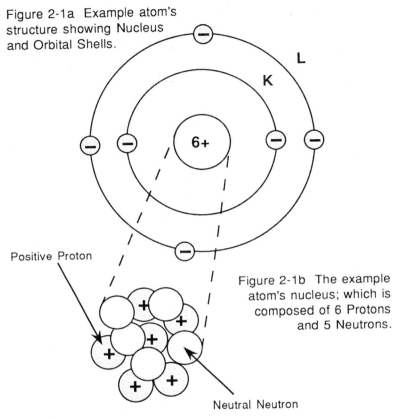

Figure 2-1a Example atom's structure showing Nucleus and Orbital Shells.

Figure 2-1b The example atom's nucleus; which is composed of 6 Protons and 5 Neutrons.

Positive Proton

Neutral Neutron

Figure 2-1 (a, b)   Atomic Construction

Suppose that a car is a compound. Then the molecules that make up the car (compound) are tires, engine, seats, etc. (molecules). The tires are made of rubber (element). If you chop up the tires into the smallest possible pieces, these would represent rubber atoms. If this is still not clear, discuss it with your friends. Understanding the differences between atoms, molecules, elements, and compounds will make the rest of this chapter much easier.

Everything we see is made up of a large number of atoms. For example, since silver is an element, the tip of a pure silver pin would be made up of thousands of silver atoms. If we keep dividing the tip into smaller and smaller particles, we will reach a stage where we cannot further divide the particle without destroying the characteristics of silver. This smallest particle of silver is called a silver atom. Thus, the atom of an

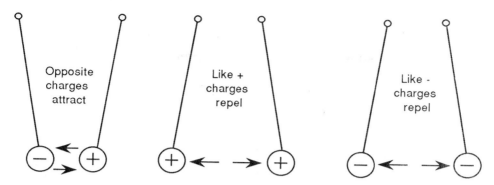

Figure 2-2   The Force between Charged Particles

element is defined as the smallest particle of the element which still possesses the characteristics of the element.

Now let's focus on the structure of an atom. As we zoom in on a single atom, we see a little group of particles in the center of a spherical shell formed by tiny orbiting particles, as shown in Figure 2-1a. Although this is not what an atom actually looks like, this representation provides us with a simple way of studying the principles of atomic structure.

If we zoom in closer, we see that the group in the middle, called the nucleus, is made up of two different kinds of particles, protons and neutrons. They look similar, as in Figure 2-1b, but have one big difference, their electrical charge. Each particle has a positive, negative, or neutral (absence of any) charge. The basic rule of charges is, as illustrated in Figure 2-2, like charges repel and opposite charges attract.

Neutral particles have no preference about the particles they associate with. The nucleus of one atom, for example, might have one proton and one neutron. The proton would have a positive charge and the neutron would be neutral. Since these are the only two components of the nucleus, it will have a positive charge. If we now zoom back a little and focus in on those high-speed, orbiting particles, we see that they are much smaller than their nuclear counterparts and we also find that they have a negative charge, as shown in Figure 2-3. They are electrons.

CHARGES AND CONDUCTIVITY

In a normal or electrically neutral atom the number of protons is equal to the number of electrons; the equal number of positive and negative charges cancel the effect of each other and the atom has no net charge. If there are more protons than electrons in the atom, the result will be a

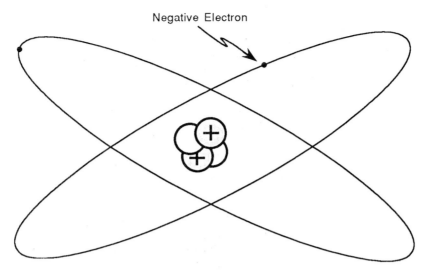

Figure 2-3   Orbiting Electrons

positively charged atom. The opposite is true if there are more electrons than protons. The charge of any atom can drastically change its behavior. When charges build up, they are said to be electrostatic. These electro-static charges are normally called static electricity and are evident every winter in cold climates. For example, when you walk across a wool carpet wearing leather-soled slippers and touch the light switch, the tiny light-ning bolt you see, hear, and feel is an electrostatic discharge. This dis-charge is the result of groups of atoms with different charges coming into close proximity with each other.

Charged atoms are called ions and are either positive or negative, depending on their condition. The size or amount of the charge is deter-mined by the difference in the numbers of particles. If there are 15 protons in the nucleus and 25 orbiting electrons, the charge is said to be -10. Examples of this are provided in Figure 2-4. Ions are the building blocks of electricity, as you will see from the following discussion.

Electrons do not just orbit around the nucleus randomly but rather are arranged into shells or levels. It has been determined that each shell has a maximum number of electrons that can orbit within it. The shells must fill from the inside progressing outward; that is, before any electrons will orbit in the second shell the first must be full. This is true for all shells.

The stability of an atom is determined by its charge and by the num-ber of electrons in its outermost shell, or valence shell. If the valence shell of an atom is filled to capacity, the atom is usually relatively stable. If the valence shell is filled to less than half of its capacity, it has a tendency to

Figure 2-4a Diagram of a Neutral Atom

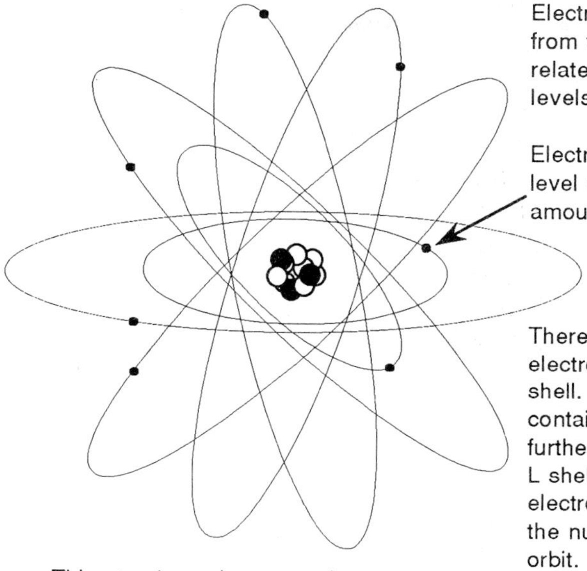

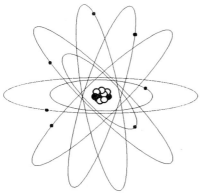

Electrons orbit at different distances from the nucleus. These distances relate to distinct electron energy levels.

Electrons orbiting in the innermost level (the K shell) possess the least amount of energy.

There is a maximum number of electrons that can exist in each shell. The innermost K shell can contain 2 electrons. The next further shell from the nucleus is the L shell which can contain up to 8 electrons. The M shell is third from the nucleus and is an 18-electron orbit. Successive shells called N, O, P, and Q are at increasing distances outward from the nucleus.

This atom's nucleus contains 7 protons and 4 neutrons

In this illustration, the K shell has 2 electrons and the L shell contains 5 electrons. The - 7 charge of the electrons is balanced by the + 7 charge from the protons that are in the nucleus.

Figure 2-4b. Sample Positive and Negative Ions

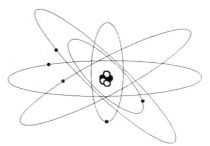

There are 4 protons and 1 neutron in the nucleus of this atom. With 5 orbiting electrons, this atom is a negative ion that has a -1 charge.

With 10 protons in the nucleus and only 7 orbiting electrons, this atom is a positive ion that has a +3 charge.

Figure 2-4 (a, b)   Electron/Proton Balance

give away some electrons or to share them with other atoms. Elements made up of such atoms are good conductors because the electrons in their valence shells tend to escape from the orbit. These electrons that no longer orbit the nucleus are called free electrons. Therefore, conductors can be defined as elements or compounds that provide easy movement of charges and transfer electrical energy readily. An example of a good conductor is copper.

If the valence shell of an atom has over half of its positions occupied, it has the tendency to borrow electrons from other atoms to fill its own shell to capacity, and thus become stable. These stable atoms do not tend to give away electrons. They discourage the movement of electrons or charges and are therefore called insulators, or nonconductors. An example of an insulator is glass.

We have now arrived at our first working definition of electricity. Electricity is the transfer of electrons or electrical charges from one atom to another.

RESISTANCE

We now know that some materials allow electrical charge movement more readily than others. The opposition that charges encounter when trying to move through a material is described as the resistance of the material. From what we know, we can conclude that insulators have a very high resistance and that conductors have a very low resistance. The unit of measurement for resistance is the ohm, named after the German scientist and teacher, George Ohm. The higher the resistance a material has, the higher its ohmic value. A particular shape of copper might have a resistance of 2 ohms but the same shape of glass might have 150 million ohms. Every material has a specific resistance value.

The resistance of a material changes as the cross-sectional area of the material changes. A larger cross-sectional area will have less resistance than a smaller one of the same material because the electrons have more space in which to move. A copper cable with a radius of 3 cm will have much less resistance than a similar cable with a radius of 1 cm.

CURRENT FLOW AND POTENTIAL DIFFERENCE

When electrons move through a material (ideally, a conductor), they can be thought of as flowing in the same way water flows through a pipe. This flow of charges is known as current and is illustrated in Figure 2-5. As electrons move through a conductor from one end to the other, they stay in the wire instead of going somewhere else because the wire provides a path of much less resistance than the insulator, the rubber or plastic that usually coats the conductor. If the conductor were bare, the electrons would still follow the path of the conductor because air is also a very good insulator. This flow is much the same as that of water, with a pipe or hose acting as the insulator.

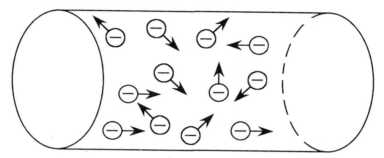

Figure 2-5a. Random Electron Motion in a Conductor

An isolated piece of wire, by itself, does not have electrons moving from one end to the other. The electrons in such a wire move in only random directions.

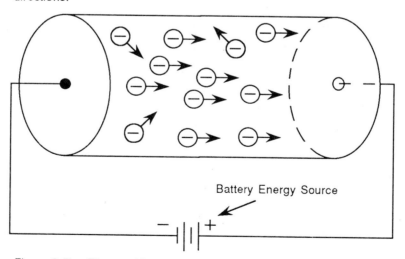

Figure 2-5b. Electron Motion in a Conductor

When an energy source is connected across the ends of the same wire an organized movement of electrons occurs.

Figure 2-5   Electron Flow Analogy

The amount of water passing through a hose is usually measured in gallons per minute. With electricity there is also a standard measure of flow or current. This standard unit of measurement is the ampere, named for André Ampère, a French physicist. One gallon per minute of water is rather self-explanatory; that is, one gallon of water goes past a specific point in one minute's time. One ampere is defined as one coulomb of electrons moving past a given point in one second. A coulomb is roughly 6,242,000,000,000,000,000 electrons.

Atoms, when they are charged, exhibit the same behavior as do many other things in nature. If you take an open bottle of carbonated beverage, put your thumb over the opening, and shake it, a force builds up inside the bottle causing the beverage to shoot everywhere when you remove your thumb. Uneven forces will always try to equalize themselves; that is, when you remove your thumb the liquid comes out of the bottle until the force inside the bottle becomes the same as that outside (force exerted by atmospheric pressure). To get electrons to move, we also need some kind of force. The interaction of positive and negative charges results in electrical force. When unlike charges are given the ability (when connected by a conductor, for instance) to come together, because of their attraction for each other they will do so. This electrical force is defined as voltage. Voltage is named after Alexandro Volta and its unit of measurement is the volt. Two separate points are defined as having one volt of charge between them if one point has one coulomb more than the other point. This concept of voltage is illustrated in Figure 2-6.

Because voltage can be thought of as electrical force, it follows that the larger the difference in voltage from one point to another, the greater the force between the points. A voltage of 100 volts is twice as great as one of 50 volts and has twice the electrical force.

OHM'S LAW

It seems that the definitions of voltage, resistance, and current must be related somehow and indeed they are. The amount of water that flows out the end of a hose is determined by the water pressure and by the ease of the water flow. In the case of electricity, the number of electrons that flow through a certain portion of a conductor (a wire, for example) is determined by the voltage applied to the circuit and by the level of resistance of the conductor. George Ohm examined these principles of electricity and developed Ohm's law, which explains how the amount of current, the resistance, and the applied voltage of a circuit are interrelated. Ohm's law

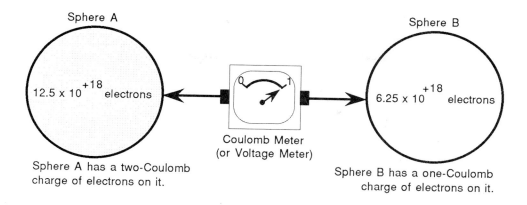

Sphere A

Sphere B

$12.5 \times 10^{+18}$ electrons

$6.25 \times 10^{+18}$ electrons

Coulomb Meter
(or Voltage Meter)

Sphere A has a two-Coulomb
charge of electrons on it.

Sphere B has a one-Coulomb
charge of electrons on it.

The meter indicates that there is one Coulomb of potential
difference between Spheres A and B — that also means a 1 volt
potential difference exists between the two spheres.

Figure 2-6   Voltage

is shown in Figure 2-7. Using some basic algebra, we can develop the other two forms of this law, as given in Figure 2-8.

It is clear from these equations that if we know the voltage and the resistance, we can calculate the current. It is also true that if we know the voltage and the current, we can calculate the resistance, and that the voltage can be calculated if current and resistance are known. Ohm's law is simple, but it is also the most powerful tool we have to determine how electricity behaves.

For example, if we wanted 2 amperes of current to flow through 4 ohms of resistance, how much voltage (electrical force) would we need? Using the algebraic equivalent of Ohm's law we can see that the following relationship exists:

Voltage = Current × Resistance or V = I R

If we substitute the values for current and resistance we get:

Voltage = 2 amperes × 4 ohms = 8 volts

As another example, say we connect a 30-volt source to a wire with a resistance of 6 ohms. What would be the current flow? Since we know that I = E/R, then I = 30/6, or 5 amperes.

In 1826, George Simon Ohm discovered how the amount of current I in a circuit depends on its resistance R and the applied voltage V .

Ohm's Law

Stated as an equation, Ohm's Law reads

$$V_{AB} = I \times R \qquad\qquad (2\text{-}1)$$

In equation 2-1, V_{AB} stands for the voltage, or potential difference, between any two points A and B in a circuit, I stands for the current moving from A to B, and R stands for the resistance between A and B.

In the more general form, the subscripts on V are dropped and Ohm's law is simply written as

$$V = I \times R$$

(R, V, and I should be calculated using units of ohms, volts, and amperes.)

Figure 2-7   Ohm's Law

As a final example, we have measured a circuit and found that the current is 5 amperes and the voltage is 100 volts. What is the resistance of the circuit? Since R = E/I, then R = 100/5, or 20 ohms.

MAGNETISM

Magnetism and electricity are closely related. As almost everyone knows, a magnet is a metallic substance (iron, steel, etc.) that, when brought near another metallic material, will either be drawn to the material or repelled away from it. This attraction or repulsion is caused by the magnetic field that surrounds the magnet. You probably remember from fourth grade

Using algebraic manipulation, Equation 2-1 can be modified for calculating current or resistance...

If a circuit's voltage and current are known, its resistance can be found by using equation 2-2.

$$R = \frac{V}{I} \qquad\qquad (2\text{-}2)$$

If a circuit's voltage and resistance are known, its current can be found by using equation 2-3.

$$I = \frac{V}{R} \qquad\qquad (2\text{-}3)$$

Remember, for each variation of Ohm's Law, the units for R, V, and I are ohms, volts, and amperes.

Figure 2-8 Other Forms of Ohm's Law

science class sprinkling the metal filings on a piece of paper and moving a magnet under the paper to see the filings line up with the lines of magnetic force. If you take a wire and pass it through the same magnetic field, an electric current is induced into the wire. Also, if several wraps of wire are wound around a steel bar, the bar will become magnetized when a current is passed through the wire. The relationship between electricity and magnetism is so close that the force field around an electromagnet is called an electromagnetic field. If you would like to know more about magnetism, many texts on basic electronics for technical personnel discuss this subject in greater detail.

CHAPTER REVIEW

On a separate sheet of paper, write a response to each question, statement, or problem below.

True or False

1. Copper wire is made up of an extremely large number of atoms.
2. The nucleus of an atom is made up of neutrons and protons.
3. The proton has a negative charge and the electron has a positive charge.
4. Neutrons are neutral particles that possess no electrical charge.
5. An atom that has its outermost shell filled with electrons would be an insulator.
6. The resistance of a wire increases as its cross-sectional area increases.
7. The potential difference, or voltage, of a circuit is analogous to water pressure in a pipe.
8. Ohm's law can be stated as R = V/I.

Short Answer

1. What is the current if 2 coulombs of electrons flow through a certain point in a wire in 1 second?
2. If the voltage of a circuit is 4 volts and the value of the resistance in the circuit is 2 ohms, how much current flows in the circuit?
3. If we want 8 amperes of current to flow through a resistance of 3 ohms, how much voltage is necessary?
4. If the potential difference between two points in a wire is 15 volts, and 3 amperes of current flow through the wire, what is the resistance of the wire between these two points?

3

Basic Components

This chapter covers the basic components of typical circuits. Wires, conductors, loads, power supplies, fuses, resistors, capacitors, and inductors are all discussed. When you understand how these components work, you have mastered analog electronics.

WIRES AND CONDUCTORS

As discussed earlier, conductors are the highways for electrons. Most metals are conductors, although some conduct better than others. Copper is the most common material used as an electrical conductor because it has excellent conductivity and is still relatively inexpensive.

The most common practical form of conductor is the wire. A wire is a conductor that has been formed into an evenly cross-sectioned cylindrical shape. Most of us are familiar with wires in the form of electrical cords. Wires come in many shapes and sizes, depending on their uses. The larger the diameter of a wire, the more current it is capable of safely conducting. Wires are commonly coated with an insulating material, usually plastic or rubber. This coating prevents the bare wires from coming in contact with each other or with another conductor.

Wires are also made from aluminum, silver, and even gold. Although gold and silver are good conductors, very few houses are wired with gold or silver (for obvious reasons). Nevertheless, because gold does not corrode, it is sometimes used to plate the contacts of certain electronic components.

Wires are classified by their diameter. The commonly accepted unit of wire size is gage. Table 3-1 lists wire dimensions and their relative resistances.

Table 3-1   Copper-Wire Table

Gage no.	Diameter, mil	Ohms per 1000 ft of copper wire at 25° C	Gage no.	Diameter, mil	Ohms per 1000 ft of copper wire at 25° C
1	289.3	0.1264	20	31.96	10.35
10	101.9	1.018	22	25.35	16.46
12	80.81	1.619	24	20.10	26.17
14	64.08	2.575	30	10.03	105.2
18	40.30	6.510	40	3.145	1069.

As you can see from the table, the higher the gage number, the smaller the diameter of the wire. Remember, smaller-diameter wire offers greater opposition to the flow of current; that is, it has more resistance.

POWER SOURCES, BATTERIES, AND POWER SUPPLIES

In Chapter 2 you learned that, for current to flow in any wire, it needs to have an electrical pressure or voltage. A device that provides current or voltage is called a source. A common source is the dry cell battery. The chemical reaction inside the battery causes electrons to build up at the negative terminal. When the circuit is completed — by turning on a flashlight, for instance — the free electrons move from the negative terminal, through the switch, through the bulb, and back to the positive terminal of the battery. If the flashlight is left on for long periods of time, the chemical reaction in the battery will gradually slow down, or exhaust itself, and will not supply electrons to the negative terminal fast enough, so the light dims. When the reaction stops, the light goes out and the battery is "dead."

When the current travels only in one direction, as it does in a circuit using a battery, it is said to be direct current, or DC. A DC circuit is demonstrated in Figure 3-1a. The other common type of source produces a current that changes direction at predetermined time intervals. This is known as alternating current, or AC, and is shown in Figure 3-1b.

The most common voltage in our homes is approximately 120 volts (V) AC. Alternating Current is used in our homes and in industry because

Direct Current (DC) where electron flow
is in one direction only (in this instance
it's from the negative to positive
terminals of the battery).

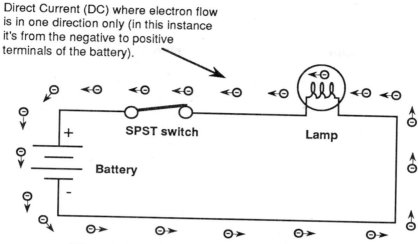

Figure 3-1a. Electron Flow in a Simple Series Circuit

Alternating Current
(AC) where electron
flow is in one direction
for half of a cycle, and
then it reverses
direction.

During negative half
cycle, direction of
electron flow reverses
(represented by
outer-most path in
Figure 3-1b).

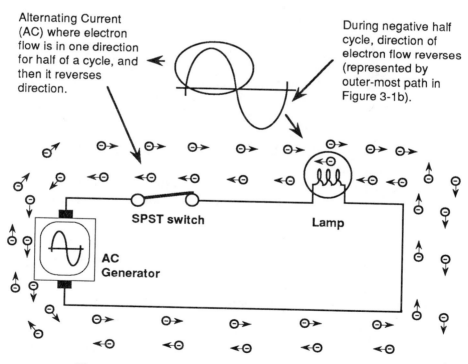

Figure 3-1b. Electron Flow in a Simple Series Circuit

Figure 3-1 (a, b)   AC and DC

it is easier to generate and transmit through wires. Two other common voltages available in this country are 220 and 440 volts; these are generally used to run equipment that requires large amounts of energy. Because the 120 V in our homes is AC, we need some way to change it into a DC voltage to operate the things that run on DC (radios, televisions, computers, and other electronic devices). The circuits that take one type of voltage and convert it into another are called power supplies. The most common power supplies take 120V AC and convert it into a DC voltage. Many of the things we use around the house actually run on DC even though they are plugged into an AC outlet in the wall. The power supplies in these devices turn the AC into DC as soon as it enters the device enclosure.

In many DC circuits, the voltage level will fluctuate up and down, but it remains DC because the electrons are always going in the same direction. In AC circuits, the electrons go in one direction for some time and then in the other for the same period. The most common AC waveform pattern is called a sine wave because it corresponds to the curve described by the mathematical sine function. Figure 3-2 shows a DC and an AC waveform. Notice the point at which the AC crosses the 0 V reference and the electrons start flowing in the opposite direction.

If we counted the number of sine waves that occur every second in our house wiring, we would see that there are 60 complete cycles each second. The unit of measurement for cycles per second is the hertz. For example, 20 cycles per second would be called 20 hertz (Hz). This notation is used for the sine and for all other AC waves as the measure of their frequency.

It may not be apparent, but the light bulbs in our homes turn off and on 120 times per second as the current changes direction. We never see the light go out because the tiny wire — called the filament — in the bulb that glows and produces light cannot cool down fast enough to go out during the brief periods of zero voltage.

LOADS AND LOADING

When you turn on the lights in your house, the filaments in the light bulbs turn electrical energy into light and heat. When the lights are turned off, the 120 V is still present at the switch but no current is flowing. When no current flows, the circuit is said to be open, or off. When the switch is turned on, the circuit is closed, or on, and current is flowing to the light bulb. The light bulb is the load for the circuit. The load for any circuit is the device that converts electrical current into other forms of energy. The current that the device draws is the load current of the circuit.

Direct Current (DC) voltage may vary, but it always stays on the same side of the zero-voltage axis (either positive, as illustrated here, or negative, but not both) so electrons move in one direction only.

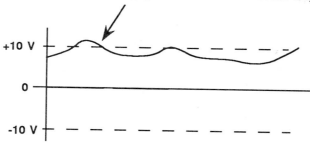

Alternating Current (AC) voltage goes across the zero-voltage axis (both positive and negative) causing the electrons to travel in two opposite directions.

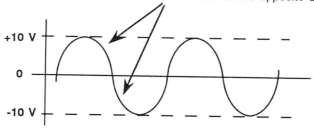

Figure 3-2   DC and AC Waveforms

Sometimes you can see the lights go dim in the house for a short period of time. This usually happens when the refrigerator, or some other device that requires a large amount of current to run, turns on. You are seeing the effects of circuit loading as the device momentarily draws a large amount of current.

Sometimes a load circuit is constructed or changed so that it draws more current than the wiring can handle or than the source is capable of supplying. When this occurs, something will usually fail. If the circuit is unprotected, something usually explodes or begins to burn. For this reason, most circuits have fuses installed in them. The purpose of a fuse is to protect any part of the circuit from currents that it cannot handle by opening the circuit before a high current can do any damage. The fuse is a thin conductor made from metal that is designed to melt at a specific current value, and is usually enclosed in glass or some other insulating material. Several common fuses are shown in Figure 3-3.

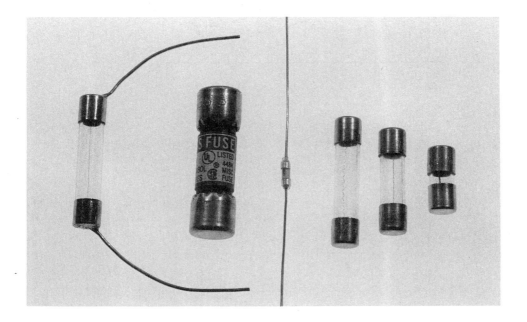

Figure 3-3   Some Common Fuses

When a current that is too large for the circuit tries to pass through
the fuse, the conductor inside the fuse will get hot and then melt apart,
causing an open circuit and stopping all current flow. The part of the
circuit that needs the large current must be repaired or changed so that
the fuse, when replaced, can handle the current.

Circuit breakers are a special type of fuse. They function just like a
fuse in the circuit but, because they are resettable, they do not have to be
replaced. If a circuit breaker opens the circuit, or trips, because of exces-
sive current, the problem can be corrected and the breaker reset to restore
normal operation. Some typical circuit breakers are pictured in Figure 3-4.

Figure 3-4 Typical Circuit Breakers

Fuses and circuit breakers come in a wide range of current ratings for any electrical power application.

RESISTORS

Resistors are probably the most commonly used electronic components. As their name implies, their purpose is to resist the flow of electrons. An iron and a toaster are examples of devices that use resistors as their main component. You can see the resistive wires in a toaster as they glow when the toast is down. These wires generate the heat that toasts the bread.

In fact, anything that has electrons flowing through it has a certain amount of resistance. Conductors have some resistance, but it is so low compared to the other resistances in the circuit that it can be disregarded in most cases. The purpose of the resistors used in circuits is to change voltage levels or to direct and control current. As current passes through a resistor, the voltage dropped across it is determined by the amount of current and the resistance of the resistor. This will be explained more fully in Chapter 4.

Resistors are made of materials that electrons have difficulty getting through. This difficulty of movement generates heat. The amount of heat is directly proportional to the current through the resistor and the voltage across it. This heat is called power. The power consumed by a resistor can be calculated as a function of the voltage and the current, or as a function of the current squared times the resistance. The two most common formulas for calculating power are given in Figure 3-5.

The unit of measurement of power is the watt. One watt of power is consumed when a resistor has one volt across it and one ampere of current flows through it.

The most common material used in resistors is carbon. Carbon, when combined with other ingredients and compressed, forms a solid that has a measurable resistance. Several common resistors are shown in Figure 3-6. Some resistors are coils of wire, while others are sheets of film made from resistive material. Regardless of the composition of the resistor, it is classified by its value in ohms and its power rating in watts. A standard system has been developed to code resistors with their value without having to write small letters and numbers on them. Color bands are placed around the body of the resistor to give its ohm value and accuracy. The resistor color code is shown in Figure 3-7. The size of the resistor generally determines its wattage, as can be seen in Figure 3-8. For resistors other than carbon type, the value and wattage are usually written on the body of the resistor.

CAPACITORS

Capacitors are electrostatic devices. They have the ability to charge up and store a voltage. To continue our water analogy, a capacitor would be like a bucket. Water (current) can go into the bucket and none will come out until the bucket is full (fully charged). The bucket can be dumped

Power is an important electrical unit. Remember that power is consumed in all components of a circuit having appreciable resistance.

The unit of power commonly used is the watt (W). **One Watt of power is used when one joule of work is done in one second of time.**

$$P = I \times V \qquad (3\text{-}1)$$

There are three standard formulas for computing the power used in any component of an electric circuit. They are no more difficult to use than is Ohm's law.

Equation 3-1 is the standard power formula. If we substitute the Ohm's law equation for V (where V = I x R), we can modify equation 3-1 to find power if current and resistance are known:

$$P = I \times (I \times R)$$

$$P = I^2 \times R \qquad (3\text{-}2)$$

Now let's assume that we know the values of current and resistance for a circuit. If we substitute the Ohm's law for I (where I = V / R) we can modify equation 3-1 to find power:

$$P = I \times V \qquad (3\text{-}1)$$

$$= \frac{V}{R} \times V$$

$$P = \frac{V^2}{R} \qquad (3\text{-}3)$$

Figure 3-5 (a, b, c)   Power Formulas

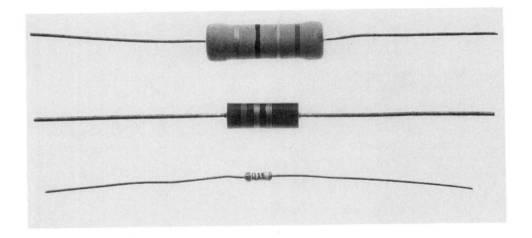

Figure 3-6 Common Resistors (Courtesy of National Semiconductors Corp.,
Santa Clara, CA)

(discharged) as needed. When a steady voltage is placed across its terminals, a capacitor will have a large current flow at the first instant because
the voltage across its leads is the same as the source voltage. As time
passes, the capacitor starts to accept the electrical charge and the difference in voltage potential between the capacitor leads and the source terminals starts to decrease, causing a decrease in current. After the capacitor
has gained a full charge, the voltage across the leads is the same as the
source voltage and the current ceases to flow. These characteristics are

Resistance Color Stripes. The use of bands or stripes is the most common system for color-coding carbon resistors, as illustrated by the diagram below:

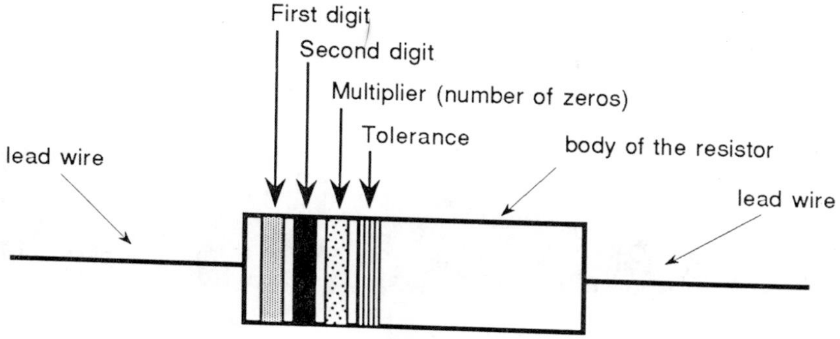

Color stripes are printed at one end of the insulating body, which is usually light brown. Reading from left to right, the band closest to the edge represents the first digit in the numerical value. The next band marks the second digit. The third band is the decimal multiplier, which indicates the number of zeros following the two digits.

Resistance Code

Color	Value	Color	Value
Black	0	Green	5
Brown	1	Blue	6
Red	2	Violet	7
Orange	3	Gray	8
Yellow	4	White	9

Tolerance Code

Color	Value
Gold	5%
Silver	10%
None	20%

Example:

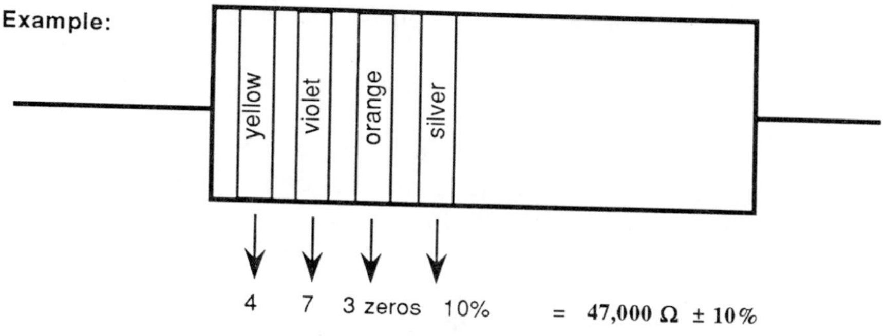

4   7   3 zeros   10%   = 47,000 Ω ± 10%

Figure 3-7   Resistor Color Code

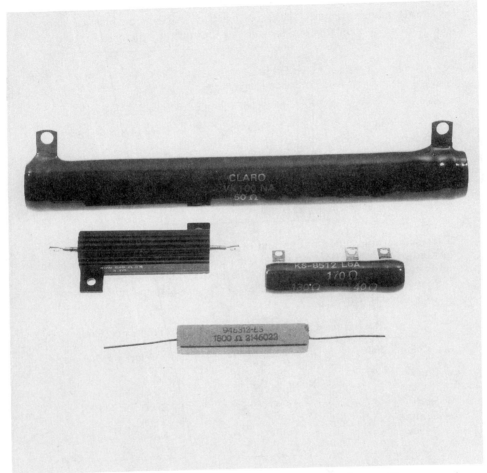

Figure 3-8   Resistor Wattages (Courtesy of National Semiconductors Corp.,
Santa Clara, CA)

shown in Figure 3-9, which includes charging and discharging curves. The
time it takes for the charging to take place is determined by the value of
the capacitor and the resistance in the circuit.

Capacitors have two values that determine their operational characteristics. They have a voltage value, which is the maximum that can be
safely placed across the device. They also have a capacitive value, which
is given in farads, the unit of measurement for capacitance. Capacitance
determines the "size" of the capacitor, that is, how fast it will charge up
and how much current it can put out when it is discharged. These two

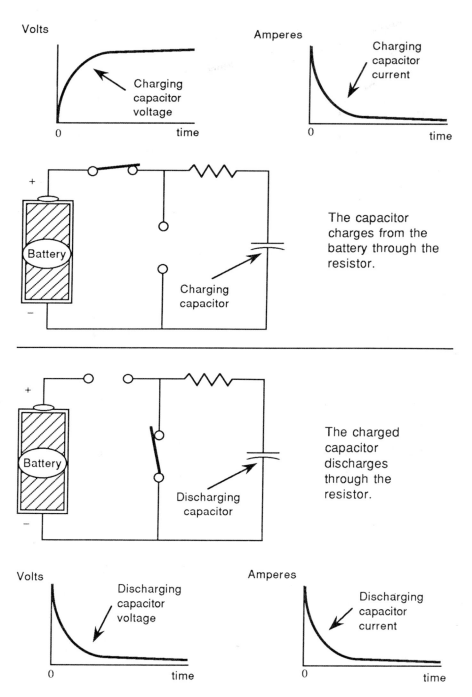

Figure 3-9   Capacitor Curves

values determine in what circuits the capacitor can be used and how it will operate in those circuits. Capacitors have a color code, in combination with letters, to identify their characteristics. In fact, there are several different color codes used for capacitors. There is a six-dot code for mica and molded-paper capacitors, a six-band code for cylindrical-paper capacitors, and at least two others. When you encounter a capacitor with a color code on it, your first task is to determine which code it is; then you can go to a reference book to decode the code. Capacitors will be covered in greater detail in the next chapter.

INDUCTORS

Inductors are electromagnetic devices. They are essentially coils of wire. The principle that gives them their unique characteristics is the ability of an electromagnetic or a magnetic field to induce a current into a conductor. This principle is called induction. Any time a current flows through a wire there is an electromagnetic field generated around the wire that is like the field generated by a magnet. Normally this field is of no consequence, but if the wires are wound very close together, they induce this field into each other. If an inductor is placed in series with a resistor and a battery, as was done with the capacitor, at the first instant voltage is applied, the field around the wire will try to expand. As this happens, the wire induces the force field into itself. This causes the inductor to have great opposition to electron movement and almost no current flow. As the field starts to expand and stabilize, the current through the coil will increase because the expanding field is not working against itself as hard. After the field is fully stabilized, the current through the inductor will be the same as that through an equal length of wire.

Just as the capacitor can be discharged after it is charged, the inductor force field collapses after the source is disconnected. This collapsing field causes a current to flow in the wire in the direction opposite to that of the energizing current, in the same manner as the capacitor. The current and voltage curves for the inductor are shown in Figure 3-10. Notice the differences between them and the capacitor curves.

The unit of measurement for inductance is the henry. It is like the farad in that it denotes the size of the inductor. Inductors, often called coils, are also sized by their maximum voltage and current. In the next chapter we will put coils into circuits and see how they work.

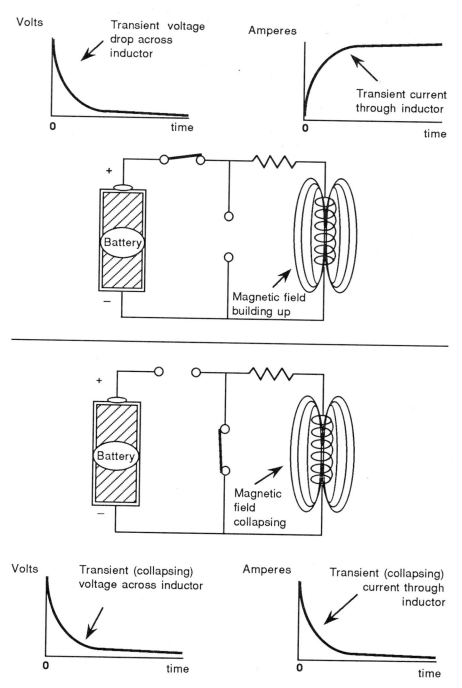

Figure 3-10   Inductor Curves

CHAPTER REVIEW

On a separate sheet of paper, write a response to each question, statement, or problem below.

True or False

1. The higher the gage number, the lower the resistance of the wire.
2. In a battery, chemical energy is converted to electrical energy.
3. Current from a dry cell battery is AC.
4. An AC current waveform is a sine wave.
5. When a load in the circuit increases above a certain limit, the fuse blows.
6. Circuit breakers are fuses that need to be replaced.
7. For a circuit, power can be calculated with the formula $P = V \times I$.

Fill in the Blank

1. The unit of measure for frequency is _____.
2. Current in a circuit flows from the _____ terminal to the _____ terminal of the battery.
3. The unit of measurement of power is the _____.
4. Capacitors are _____ devices, while inductors are _____ devices.

Short Answer

1. Explain the function of a power supply.
2. What is the difference between an AC and a DC current?
3. What is the difference between a closed circuit and an open circuit?
4. Describe the charging operation of a capacitor.
5. If a capacitor gets fully charged, the current in the circuit decreases. Why?
6. Describe the principle of induction.
7. What are the units of measurement for capacitance and inductance?

4

DC Circuits

INTRODUCTION

The purpose of this chapter is to give you some appreciation of the complexity of even simple circuits and some understanding of the tools and formulas used to analyze them.

BASIC CIRCUITS — MORE OHM'S LAW

Any connection of electrical components that provides a path for current is called a circuit; most circuits have many current paths or branches. Because it is often not convenient or possible to draw a picture of circuit components, a system of symbols has been developed for use in electrical diagrams. The total circuit diagram with these symbols is called a schematic diagram. Figure 4-1 illustrates the schematic symbols for several common electrical components.

The simplest circuits consist of a source, a load, and the wires (conductors) connecting them, as shown in Figure 4-2. Using Ohm's law, we can see that if the resistance of the bulb and the applied voltage are known, the amount of current that will flow in the circuit can be calculated. Let's assume that the bulb's resistance is 10 ohms. If the $I = E/R$ form of Ohm's law is used, as shown in Figure 4-3, the current is equal to 1.5 A (amperes). The resistance of the wires is disregarded in the calculations because it is very small compared to the resistance of the bulb. If, for some reason, a circuit had been constructed with the wire conductor, but without a light bulb or any other load, the result would be a short circuit. The term "short" suggests that the current is following an undesirable path of low resistance (usually an accidental condition).

Figure 4-4 is a schematic diagram for a circuit having a jumper wire connected from the positive to the negative terminal of the battery. The bulb will not glow because the current will flow through the wire instead

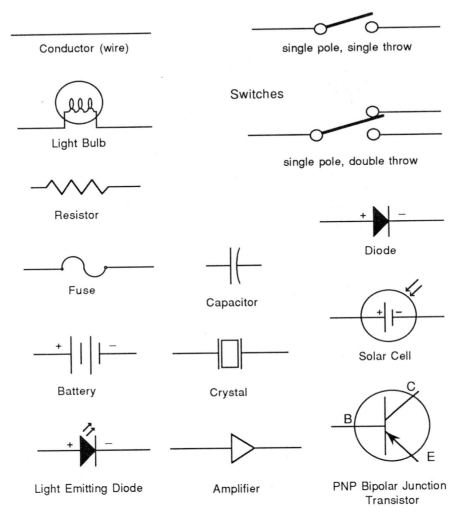

Figure 4-1   Schematic Diagram Symbols

of the bulb. This is called shorting across the battery or shorting around the bulb.

An arc or some other display of excess heat or energy will appear if the source in the circuit has a high voltage or current capacity. When a short occurs, the total effective resistance of the circuit is reduced to almost zero. The only resistance present in the circuit is that of the wires and the internal resistance of the battery. This forces the battery to supply the maximum amount of current that it is capable of producing. The

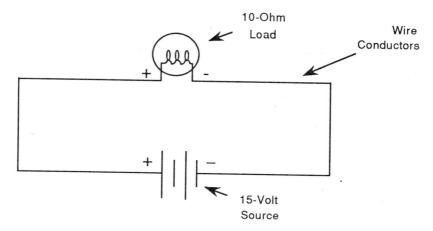

10-Ohm
Load

Wire
Conductors

+

−

+

−

15-Volt
Source

Figure 4-2   A Basic Circuit

reason can be easily demonstrated by substituting the voltage of the battery and zero resistance into the I = V/R form of Ohm's law. The division of any real number by zero produces an infinite value (or an error indication, if you use a calculator). This high current will cause the wires to heat up or even to burn if the battery has enough amperage. Many household fires are caused by such arcing or overheating when the fuses or circuit breakers in the circuit are not operating properly.

Let's take the same circuit but change the values. Let the current in the circuit equal 0.25 A and the resistance of the bulb equal 15 ohms. Use a different form of Ohm's law to figure the voltage of the source. Did you get 3.75 V? If not, try again. Figure 4-5 includes a schematic diagram and a problem solution for this circuit. Check your answer by taking the 3.75 V and dividing it by 0.25 A. You should get 15 ohms, which is the resistance of our bulb.

You now know how to calculate volts, ohms, and amperes in circuits, but you need some idea what these things are and what they mean. Many flashlight batteries provide 1.5 volts (sizes D, C, A, AA, and AAA). The physical size of the battery indicates how much material is inside, which

$$I = \frac{E}{R} = \frac{15 \text{ volts}}{10 \text{ ohms}} = 1.\,5 \text{ amperes}$$

Figure 4-3   Ohm's Law Equation

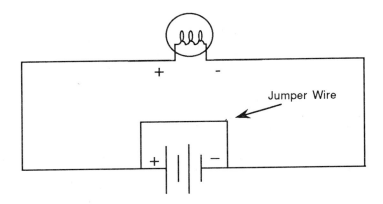

Figure 4-4   Shorting Across a Battery

determines the current-producing capability of the particular battery.
There are some small, rectangular batteries that produce 9 and 22 volts. It
is unlikely that a 1.5 V battery would ever cause a noticeable shock, but if
you were installing a new 22 V battery and your fingers were wet, contact
by one finger to each terminal of the battery could cause you to experience
a mild shock — you allowed your fingers to become the conductor for the
battery current.

Circuit :

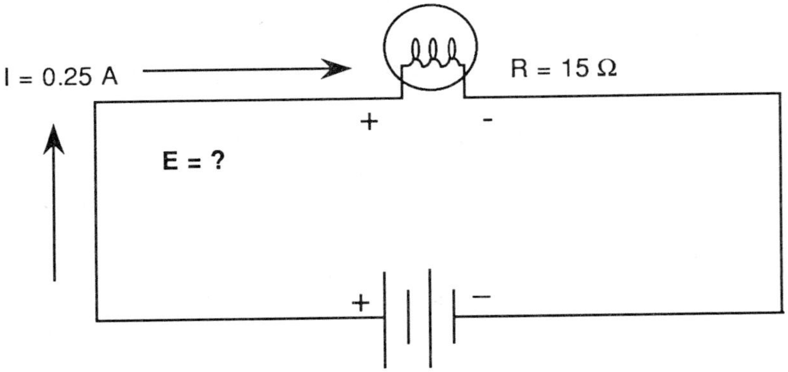

I = 0.25 A ⟶   R = 15 Ω

E = ?

Solution *(using Ohm's Law)* :

$$E = I \cdot R = (0.25 \text{ A}) (15 \text{ Ω}) = 3.75 \text{ volts}$$

Figure 4-5   Circuit and Solution

The electrical system in a car, unless it is very old or a nonstandard foreign one, will be a 12-volt system and is generally not capable of producing a shock. However, the spark coil in the ignition system generates several-thousand-volt voltage spikes to ignite the fuel mixture in the engine cylinders and will provide quite a jolt if one of the spark plug wires is touched with the engine running. Although such a shock can be quite painful, the automotive spark coil seldom has the amperage necessary to kill a person.

Normal house wiring carries 120 and 240 V, depending on the system. Both of these household voltages can conduct enough current through the body to cause electrocution. They are potentially deadly and should not be fooled with. The common voltage found atop the average utility pole is 4,160 V. The amperage that can be supplied by the utility pole at this voltage level is usually deadly upon contact and any power linesperson can tell stories that would impress even the most skeptical.

The resistance of a one-foot length of average house wire is around 0.0001 ohm (it varies somewhat as its diameter or gage changes). This is not too much, but then it shouldn't be: it's a conductor. The speakers of an average stereo system are generally rated at 8 ohms. A 60-watt light bulb, when not hot, has a resistance of 31 ohms. The value of most electrical insulators is in the 1-million to 100-million ohm range. These values are provided to give the reader some concept of the meaning and magnitude of an ohm.

What about currents? An average house with several lights on and normal appliances running (refrigerator, clocks, and personal computer) will draw from 5 to 15 A. An average radio will use about 0.05 A, but a boom box playing a tape at full volume can draw as much as 0.3 A — its batteries won't last long, though.

Almost all circuits can be turned off and on. The switch is the most common component used for this function. Switches are classified by the number of contacts and the number of positions that they have. Figure 4-6 shows several switch types and their schematic symbols.

Switches are designed to satisfy a variety of needs. The common light switch remains in one position until it is manually moved to the other position (off-on). Most push buttons are normally open or normally closed, depending on their application. When the button is depressed, the opposite condition occurs. Mercury is a common switch material because it is a liquid metal at room temperature and a good conductor. It is used for position or motion applications like automobile alarms, thermostats, and no-click light switches.

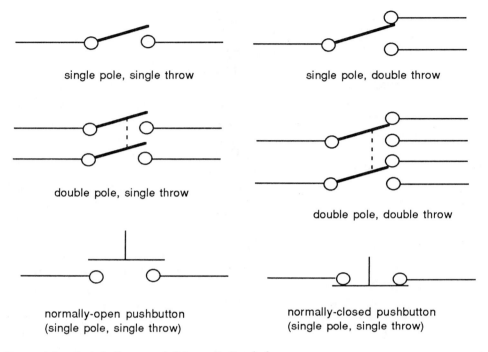

single pole, single throw   single pole, double throw

double pole, single throw

double pole, double throw

normally-open pushbutton   normally-closed pushbutton
(single pole, single throw)   (single pole, single throw)

Figure 4-6   Switch Types and Schematic Symbols

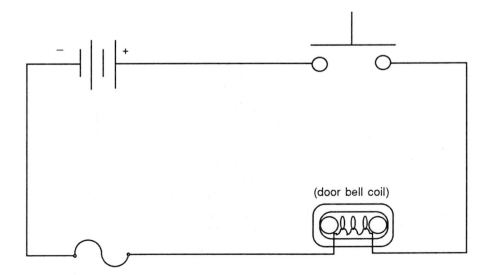

(door bell coil)

Figure 4-7   Doorbell Circuit

Figure 4-7 shows a circuit with a battery, a switch, a doorbell coil, and a fuse. When the switch is closed, the bell will ring. With a source voltage of 50 V and a bell resistance of 30 ohms, what is the current when the switch is closed? The answer is 1.667 A. What would happen if a 1-A fuse was installed in the circuit? A perfectly good fuse would be sacrificed in the interest of science.

SERIES AND PARALLEL CIRCUITS

If several lamps are placed in one circuit, they may be connected in many different ways. If they are connected so that there is only one current path, they are said to be hooked up in series. Figure 4-8a illustrates a typical series circuit. If the current is allowed to split so that some goes to each light, a parallel circuit results. Figure 4-8b is this type of circuit. Any other hookup is a variation of the series/parallel scheme. A typical series/parallel circuit is shown in Figure 4-8c.

When components are connected to one another, certain rules can be applied to determine the characteristics of the entire circuit. Resistors in series add to total resistance. The total equivalent resistance for the circuit in Figure 4-9 is 260 ohms. The magnitude of current flowing through a series circuit is the same at any point in the circuit. Because the same current is passing through all three resistors, a total circuit current value can be calculated by dividing the total source voltage by the total circuit resistance, as demonstrated in Figure 4-10.

For parallel circuits, current flow calculations are different. If the same three resistors were hooked up in parallel, as in Figure 4-11, consider what would happen. The current would leave the negative terminal of the battery and go to the first junction, or node (point A). At this point the current would divide. Now the path-of-least-resistance rule takes effect. The value of R_1 compared to the resistance of the rest of the circuit determines how much current will go through R_1 and how much will proceed to point B. The formula for calculating total resistance of parallel resistors is $R_t = (1) / [(1/R_1) + (1/R_2) + \bullet \bullet \bullet + (1/R_n)]$. If you use a calculator, you will find the total equivalent resistance of this parallel circuit to be 8 ohms.

If the circuit had only a 10-ohm resistor, all of the current would go through this resistor. When the 50-ohm resistor was added, another current path was provided, one that offered considerably more resistance, so that most of the current would still go through the 10-ohm resistor. To find out how much current, take the voltage across the resistor (50 volts) and

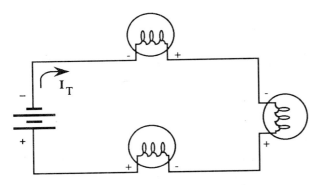

Figure 4-8a   Series Circuit

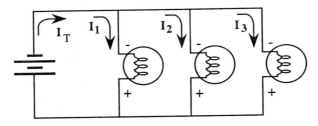

Figure 4-8b   Parallel Circuit

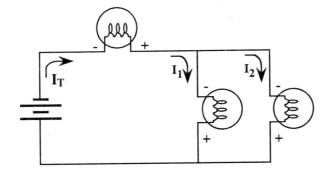

Figure 4-8c   Series _and_ Parallel Circuit

Figure 4-8 (a, b, c)   Series and Parallel Circuits

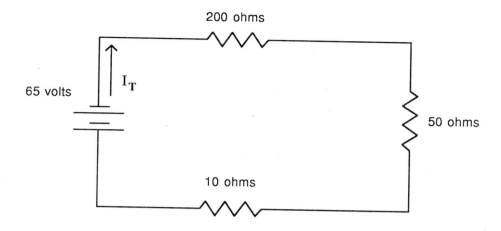

200 ohms

65 volts

I_T

50 ohms

10 ohms

$$R_T = 10 \text{ ohms} + 50 \text{ ohms} + 200 \text{ ohms}$$
$$= 260 \text{ ohms}$$

Figure 4-9   Series Resistors

divide it by the resistance (10 ohms) to get a value of 5 A. If the same is done for the 50-ohm resistor, the current calculated is 1 A, and 0.25 A is the current through the 200-ohm resistor. If the three currents are added, we get a total of 6.25 amperes. The source voltage, 50 volts, divided by the

Total circuit current $(I_T) = \dfrac{\text{Total source voltage } (V)}{\text{Total resistance } (R_T)}$

$= \dfrac{65 \text{ volts}}{260 \text{ ohms}}$

$= 0.25 \text{ amperes}$

Figure 4-10   Current Calculations for a Series Circuit

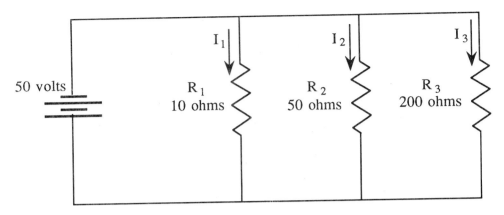

Figure 4-11   Parallel Circuit Paths

total current, 6.25 amperes, equals 8 ohms, which is what we calculated for total resistance with our formula. This is shown in Figure 4-12.

A critical concept of circuit voltages was passed by too lightly and needs some explanation here. In the series circuit, the source voltage was across all three resistors combined, so that each resistor dropped some portion of the total voltage. This voltage drop can be computed by the same method as the parallel resistance currents. Since the common current can be computed by dividing 50 V by 260 ohms, this current value of 0.192 A multiplied by each resistance value gives the voltage drop across the respective resistor. When these voltage drops are added together, they total 50 volts, the source voltage (with some round-off error possible). This leads us to the topic of laws for series and parallel circuits.

KIRCHOFF'S LAWS

Two laws, one for voltages and one for currents, allow for the analysis of most circuits. Kirchoff's voltage law states that the algebraic sum of the voltages in any closed circuit loop must equal zero. Look at the circuits in Figures 4-13a and b. Start at point A (in Figure 4-13a) and make a clockwise loop through the battery and the branch with R_1 and R_2. Keep a close eye on the plus and minus signs (polarity), as they indicate whether to add or subtract the voltage from the total. Starting at point A, go to the left and then up to the battery.

The plus sign is encountered first, so the voltage at this point is +75 V. Continue out the top of the battery, right, and down into R_1. Here the negative sign is first and the voltage is 12.5 V. This leaves the running total

$$I_1 = \frac{V}{R_1} \qquad I_2 = \frac{V}{R_2} \qquad I_3 = \frac{V}{R_3}$$

$$= \frac{50 \text{ volts}}{10 \text{ ohms}} \qquad = \frac{50 \text{ volts}}{50 \text{ ohms}} \qquad = \frac{50 \text{ volts}}{200 \text{ ohms}}$$

$$= 5 \text{ A} \qquad = 1 \text{ A} \qquad = 0.25 \text{ A}$$

$$\text{Total current } (I_T) = I_1 + I_2 + I_3$$
$$= 5 \text{ A} + 1 \text{ A} + 0.25 \text{ A}$$
$$= 6.25 \text{ A}$$

$$\text{Total resistance } (R_T) = \frac{\text{Total source voltage } (V_T)}{\text{Total current } (I_T)}$$
$$= \frac{50 \text{ V}}{6.25 \text{ A}}$$
$$= 8 \ \Omega$$

Figure 4-12 Parallel Currents

at 62.5 V. Continuing down to R_2, we find another negative sign and 62.5 V. This leaves the total voltage at 0 V and closes the loop at point A. Now do this for all other loops in this circuit and ensure that each loop is equal to 0 V.

The other of Kirchoff's laws is the current law, which states that the algebraic sum of all currents entering and leaving any node (point or connection in the circuit) must equal zero. Now look at Figure 4-13b to verify this law. Examine point B. The current entering the point is 0.715A from the battery. The current leaving this point is 0.417A to R_1 and 0.298A to R_2. The total current is 0 A.

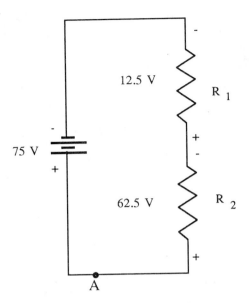

Figure 4-13a   Kirchoff's Voltage Law

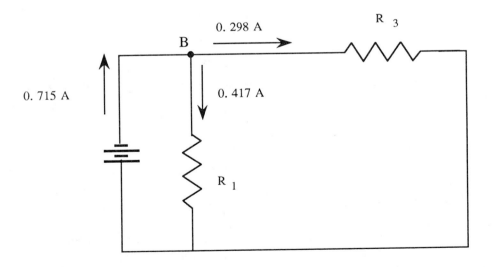

Figure 4-13b   Kirchoff's Current Law

Figure 4-13 (a, b)   Series/Parallel Circuits

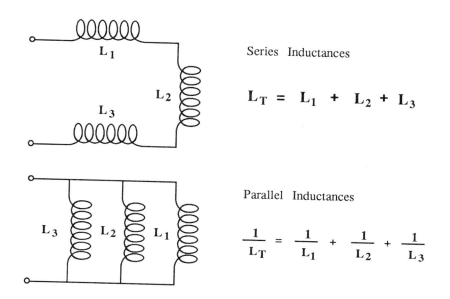

Series Inductances

$$L_T = L_1 + L_2 + L_3$$

Parallel Inductances

$$\frac{1}{L_T} = \frac{1}{L_1} + \frac{1}{L_2} + \frac{1}{L_3}$$

Figure 4-14   Inductors in Series and Parallel Circuits

OTHER COMPONENTS

We will now look at inductors and capacitors in series and parallel circuits and determine their interactions. Inductors have a similar relationship to that of resistors for calculating total magnitudes of several in series or parallel circuits. See Figure 4-14 for the formulas for inductors.

The formulas used for capacitors are the reverse of those used for resistors and inductors. Figure 4-15 shows the formulas needed for capacitors in both types of circuits. This reversal makes sense when you realize that an inductor is similar in construction to a wire-wound resistor, but a capacitor is an open circuit to a constant DC voltage. After the charging cycle, an inductor is nothing more than a wire resistor and a capacitor has no current flow in a DC circuit.

OTHER CIRCUIT ANALYSIS TOPICS

There are several circuit analysis theorems available to those who are interested in further study. Thevenin's theorem, Norton's theorem, and the superposition theorem are all indispensable tools for circuit analysis but are beyond the scope of this text. Another topic worth mentioning at

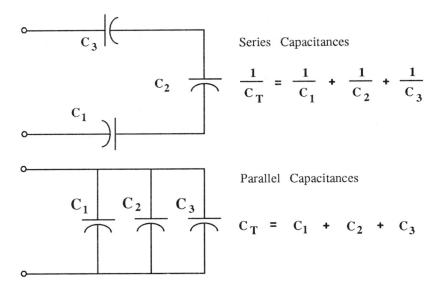

Series Capacitances

$$\frac{1}{C_T} = \frac{1}{C_1} + \frac{1}{C_2} + \frac{1}{C_3}$$

Parallel Capacitances

$$C_T = C_1 + C_2 + C_3$$

Figure 4-15   Capacitors in Series and Parallel Circuits

this time is the current flow theory. Up to this point, we have shown circuits with electrons flowing from the negative terminal of the battery or source to the positive terminal. There is a similar but opposite theory called the current flow theory. It describes the action in a circuit as a current that flows from the positive terminal to the negative terminal. The current theory parallels all of the other theories and tools, except that all of the signs are backwards. There is no operational difference between the two theories and since we cannot see which way current flows, we will not discuss this topic any further.

CHAPTER REVIEW

On a separate sheet of paper, write a response to each question, statement, or problem below.

Short Answer

   1.   A heater with a resistance of 20 ohms is connected to a 120-volt power line. How much current flows in this circuit?
   2.   What is a fuse, and why is it used in a circuit?

3. Describe Kirchoff's voltage and current laws.

4. Calculate the voltage of a circuit if the current is 4 amperes and the resistance is 3 ohms.

5. Calculate R when the voltage is 10 volts and the current is 2 amperes.

5

AC Circuits

INTRODUCTION

All of the wiring in your house or apartment is AC, all of the wiring on the poles outside it is AC, and there are many other applications for AC circuits. Because Alternating Current (AC) is all around us, an understanding of how these circuits work is of considerable value.

DIFFERENCES BETWEEN AC AND DC

Although many of the principles of DC circuits are the same for AC, there are some significant differences. Figure 5-1a is a graph of a DC voltage versus time. Compare this to the normal AC waveform shown in Figure 5-1b. The waveforms plotted in Figure 5-1 have time as the independent variable (the x axis) and voltage as the dependent variable (the y axis). This is the traditional voltage waveform, but current is also commonly shown on graphs of this type. A waveform is simply a graph of a voltage, or current plotted against time.

The difference between AC and DC can generally be attributed to the way in which the voltage was generated. DC usually comes from a battery or a power supply. A battery generates DC voltage directly from a chemical reaction, while a power supply converts it from another form of energy. An AC voltage is usually produced by rotating a coil of wire within a magnetic field.

Any magnet has around it a relatively constant electromagnetic force field. You have probably seen experiments in basic physics with a magnet and a paper with metal filings. When the paper is brought over the magnet, the filings align with lines of flux in the field. If the same filings were brought over a DC electromagnet, the force field seen would be the same. In fact, whenever a current is sent through a wire, it generates a force field around the wire. It is also true that if a wire is moved within a magnetic

DC or Direct Current at a magnitude of 9 volts (perhaps the potential difference of a transistor-radio battery?)
+10 V
0
-10 V
0
1
2
3
4
5
Time
(in seconds)

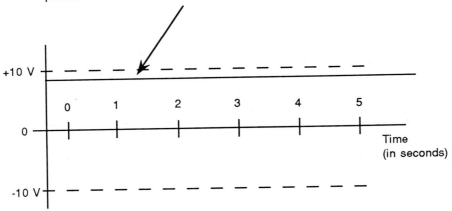

Figure 5-1a DC Voltage Versus Time

Alternating Current (AC) voltage goes across the zero-voltage axis (both positive and negative) causing the electrons to travel in two opposite directions.
+10 V
0
-10 V
0
1
2
3
4
5
Time
(in seconds)

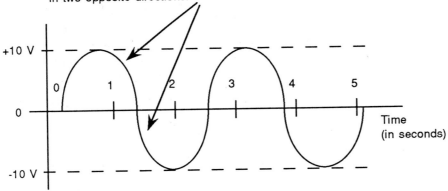

Figure 5-1b AC Voltage Versus Time

Figure 5-1 (a, b) DC and AC Waveforms

In this illustration, the conductor is pushed downward through the lines of magnetic flux, which flow from a magnet North pole toward a South pole.

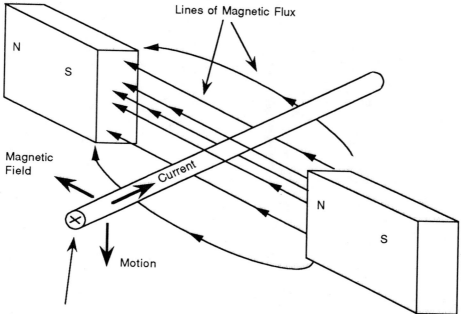

Current flow into a conductor is shown by an X which represents the tail feathers of an arrow pointing in the direction of the induced current.

If an an induced current would flow in the opposite direction, or out of the page, it would be represented by the symbol •. The dot, or bullet, is to represent the tip of an arrow flying toward you.

If the conductor in this example were moved in the opposite direction (upward), then current would also flow in a reversed direction (out toward you).

Figure 5-2   Inducing a Current into a Wire

field, current is made to flow (induced) in the wire, as illustrated in Figure 5-2.

  If a coil of wire is constructed on a shaft and rotated within a magnetic field, as shown in Figure 5-3, the voltage waveform that is generated will be the classic AC sine wave. As the rotation is started, a voltage is induced in the wire and causes current to flow. While rotation continues, the induced voltage and current increase until the voltage reaches its

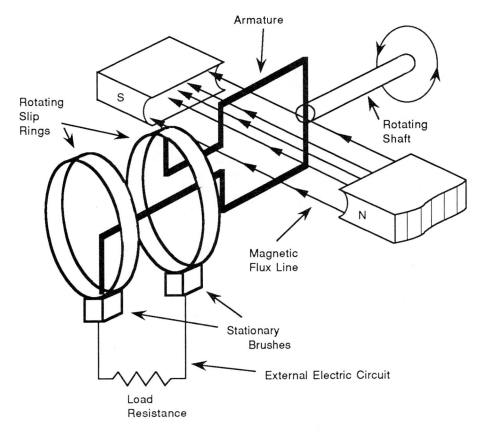

Figure 5-3   A Simple Alternator

highest point (its peak voltage). At that time, the motion of the wire is perpendicular to the lines of flux of the magnetic field so the interaction is the strongest. As rotation continues, the wire cuts the flux lines at lesser angles so the voltage decreases. At the point where the movement of the wire is nearly parallel to the lines of flux, there is no voltage induced and we are back to a point of no voltage or current, but we have only completed one half-turn of the shaft.

As shaft rotation is continued, the voltage and current start to increase again, but since the flux lines from the opposite pole are being cut, the voltage is of the opposite polarity and the current flow is in the opposite direction. Now look at the waveform in Figure 5-4 and study the voltage curve generated by one revolution of the shaft. This is the same waveform generated by the alternator in a car, or a hydroelectric, fossil-fuel, or nuclear-powered electrical energy generating plant.

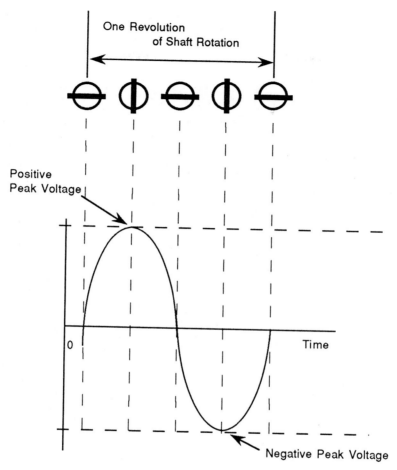

Figure 5-4   Typical AC Waveform

When only one coil of wire is used to generate the voltage, only one waveform results; this waveform is called single-phase AC voltage. What would happen if three wires were wound around our shaft at 120-degree spacing, as diagramed in Figure 5-5? The resulting three waveforms would look like those in Figure 5-6 when the shaft was rotated. This is called three phase because there are three voltages that are all the same except that they are going high and low at different times.

The definition of phase is the relationship between things that are happening at the same time. Think about a capacitor circuit. Remember that at the first instant voltage was applied, the voltage across the capacitor was very low but the current was very high. Recall also that as time

By having three separate coils equally spaced around the armature by 120 electrical degrees, each of the coils' generated voltages will also be spaced 120 electrical degrees apart.

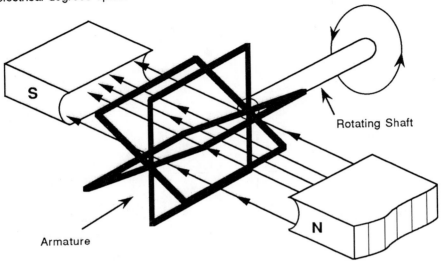

Figure 5-5   Three-phase Shaft Windings

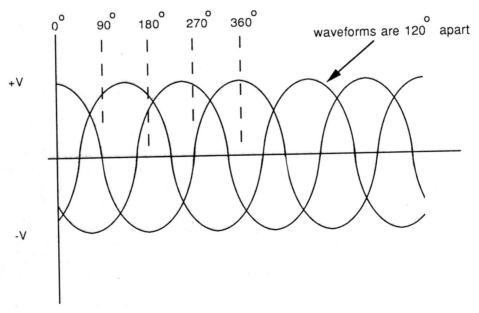

Figure 5-6   Typical Three-phase Waveform

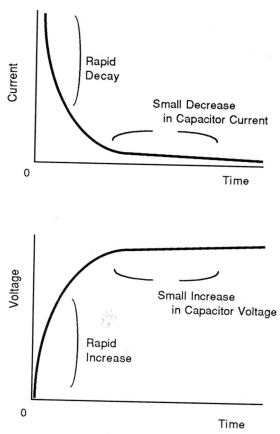

Figure 5-7   Capacitor-charging Waveforms

went by the voltage increased as the current decreased until the voltage was equal to the source and the current had stopped because of no difference of potential between the source and the capacitor leads.

Figure 5-7 is a graph of voltage and current on the same time axis as it would occur in our capacitor circuit. Now let's apply an AC sine-wave voltage to the capacitor and look at the voltage and current in the circuit. Figure 5-8 is a graph of voltage *across* and *current* through the capacitor, shown on the same set of axes. They are both sine waves but they are out of phase with each other. Careful inspection will show that the current curve is 90° ahead of the voltage curve. The general rule is that in a capacitive circuit the current leads the voltage by 90°. This is a function of the charging time of the capacitor.

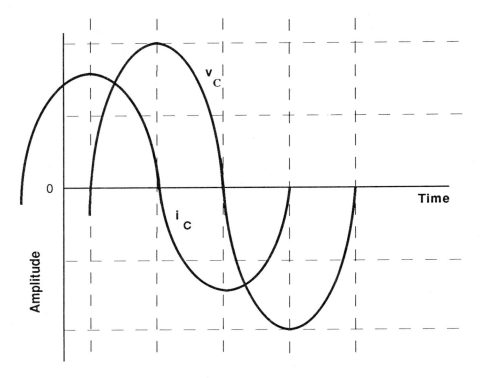

Figure 5-8   AC Applied to a Capacitive Circuit

Combining this new knowledge about capacitors with what you already know about inductors, try to predict the phase relationship in a purely inductive circuit. Figure 5-9 contains the voltage and current waveforms for an inductive circuit. With this information, construct a graph of the voltage and current in an inductive circuit with a sine wave applied, and determine the phase relationship between the two.

You should remember that resistance is the opposition electrons must overcome as they travel through electric circuits. The opposition of inductive and capacitive devices is different for DC and AC voltages, as you can see. The opposition of a resistor to DC, as we know, is called resistance, but the opposition of a capacitor or inductor to AC is called reactance. It is important to know the reactance when designing AC circuits so that the proper components are selected to allow the circuit to work properly. When resistors, capacitors, and inductors are used together in AC circuits, resistance and reactance are both present. The combination of resistance and reactance is called impedance, which is the total opposition to current flow in an AC circuit.

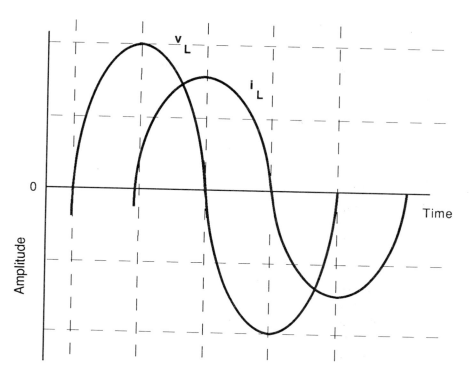

Figure 5-9   Current and Voltage in an Inductive Circuit

RECTIFICATION

Rectification is the process of converting an AC voltage into a DC voltage. This is done by using components that allow current to flow only in one direction. This clips off one half of the sine wave and keeps the voltage from changing polarity. The electrical device that allows current to flow in one direction only is known as a diode (Figure 5-10).

Look at the circuit in Figure 5-11. Study the relationship between the input and the output waveform. Since current can flow in only one direction, only half of the signal gets through; since it is all of the same polarity, it meets our definition for DC.

Now look at Figure 5-12 and consider its output waveform. All of the humps are now on top of the zero voltage level so the voltage is DC, but it varies greatly in amplitude. These two rectifiers are called half-wave and full-wave, respectively. Later on, we will discuss filter circuits that smooth out this pulsating DC voltage.

Schematic Symbol

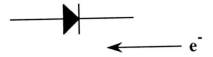

Electrons can only flow in the
direction of the arrow.

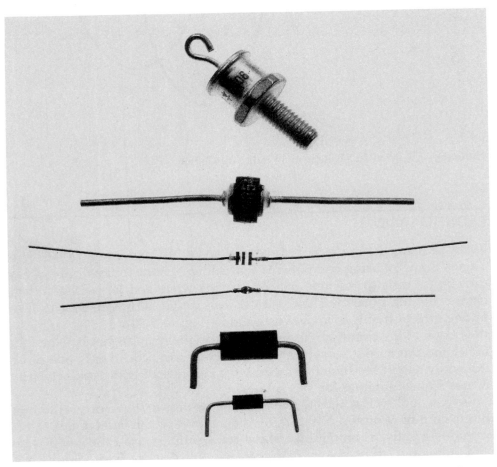

Figure 5-10   Diodes (Courtesy of National Semiconductors Corp., Santa Clara, CA)

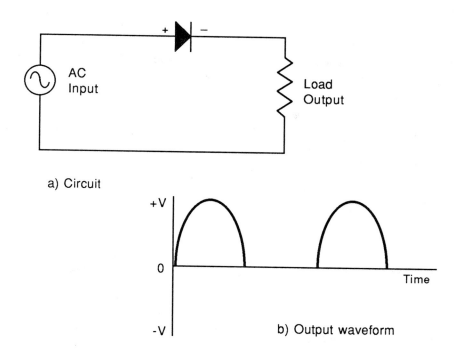

a) Circuit

b) Output waveform

Figure 5-11 (a, b) Half-wave Rectifier

TRANSFORMERS

Transformers are really just inductors wound very close to each other on an iron core so that they induce voltage and current efficiently. Figure 5-13 shows the schematic symbol and several small transformers. The input winding is called the primary and the output winding(s) is(are) the secondary. Transformers are found in all sorts of electrical and physical designs. The relationship between the input and output windings determines the voltage and current capabilities of the device. Figure 5-14 contains three common transformer designs.

The size of the wire used, the insulation between the wires, and the core size generally determine the power that the transformer will handle. The ratio of turns from the primary to the secondary determines the voltage input/output ratio. If the secondary has twice as many turns as the primary, the magnitude of the output voltage will be twice the magnitude of the input voltage. A transformer may seem like a voltage source; however, as its name implies, all the transformer really does is change the

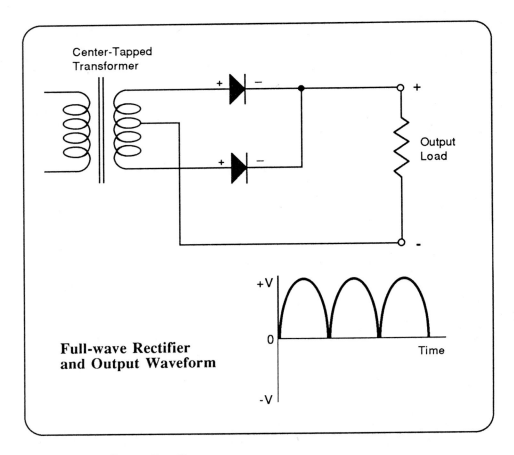

Figure 5-12   Full-wave Rectifier

value of one electrical parameter at the expense of another. For example, when the number of turns in the secondary is twice the number in the primary, the output voltage is twice the input voltage but the output current is *half* the input current. The inverse is also true — fewer turns in the secondary mean less voltage but more current capability. From this it should be easy to understand why the wire sizes of the primary and secondary may differ significantly.

Because transformers use expanding and collapsing electrical fields to transfer energy, they can be used only on AC circuits. If a transformer were placed in a DC circuit, the primary field would expand, causing the secondary field to expand; and when both fields stabilized there would be no voltage induced into the secondary windings. Transformers work only on signals with varying voltage magnitudes.

Schematic Symbol

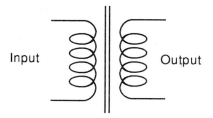

Input   Output

Figure 5-13   Transformers

RESONANCE

Resonance is the condition that occurs when the capacitance and inductance in a circuit are in balance. This occurs when the capacitive and inductive reactances become equal at a particular frequency (called the resonant frequency for that circuit). Capacitive reactance and inductive reactance are by nature opposite to each other. Therefore, when an equal amount of each is present in the same circuit, they effectively cancel each

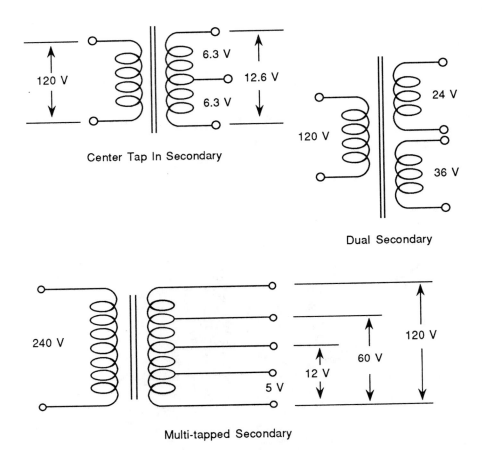

Figure 5-14   Common Transformer Configurations

other out. In other words, the only opposition that the resonant frequency encounters in the circuit is purely resistive. The results of this state are either an unusually high or an unusually low circuit output current, depending on the type of circuit. A series circuit will result in a high current and a parallel circuit will give a low current at their respective resonant frequencies.

These types of circuits have many applications. They are commonly found in transmission and reception circuits used in radio and television. They are also used in filter circuits, as they can be designed to be very sensitive to certain frequencies. Such filter provides maximum output at the resonant frequency, but minimizes the amount of output at any other frequency that is above or below resonance.

CHAPTER REVIEW

On a separate sheet of paper, write a response to each question, statement, or problem below.

Short Answer

1. What is the difference between an AC and a DC voltage?
2. Explain the function of a basic alternator.
3. What is the difference between half-wave and full-wave rectification?

True or False

1. Diodes are used for rectification.
2. Tuning is an application of resonance.
3. The output of a resonant circuit is minimum at the resonant frequency.

6

Basic Applications

INTRODUCTION

You are now ready to learn how electricity and electronics are used to make our lives easier and better. This chapter begins with a discussion of test equipment, the tools used to build, test, and troubleshoot circuits. The remainder of the chapter covers common motors and how they work. Several types of common motors will be presented, from the mixer used in the kitchen, to the garage door opener, to the alternator under the hood of your car.

TEST EQUIPMENT

We have discussed the voltages, currents, and resistances in AC and DC circuits; we have calculated their values by using formulas derived from theories and laws. To verify our calculations and to measure these values in operating circuits, we need some type of instrument that can be inserted into the circuit to gather information.

Multimeters

When properly connected in a circuit, a multimeter will measure voltage, resistance, or current, depending on its connections and settings. Digital and analog are the two basic types of multimeters. The digital meter reads out in numbers; that is, when connected properly in the circuit it will read out 10 V, 2 mA, or whatever is appropriate. Digital meters are complex devices that are relatively new. We will not discuss the inner workings of the digital meter here, except to say that it uses digital circuitry and sampling to obtain readings. Analog meters have a pointer or needle that moves across a numbered face to indicate the reading. When the pointer stops moving, or is stable enough to read, the value is read from the numbers printed on the face of the meter.

The position of the pointer is determined by a tiny coil of wire that is connected to the pointer. This setup is called a D'Arsonval meter movement and is the heart of all analog meters. When a small current is run through the coil, the force field that is created reacts with the field of a small magnet, which causes the coil and its attached pointer to move. This current must be carefully controlled using resistors in series and parallel with the coil as the coil is made of very fine wire that cannot handle much current.

There are rules and guidelines concerning each type of measurement. Let's start with voltage. Voltage is always measured across the component(s) to be checked. Since voltage is dropped across any component because of its resistance, the voltmeter is always connected in *parallel* with the section of the circuit to be checked. Figure 6-1 shows the proper con-

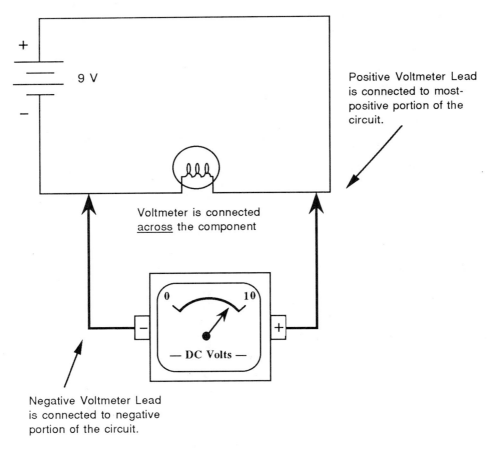

Figure 6-1   Voltmeter Connection

nection of a voltmeter in a circuit. The analog voltmeter operates by placing a high value of resistance in parallel with the voltage to be measured and uses the current that flows through it to determine the value of the circuit voltage. Since the resistance of the meter is very high compared to the resistance of the circuit, the effects of the added resistance are often negligible. Figure 6-2 shows the circuitry inside the basic voltmeter. The value of the dropping resistor is changeable and is determined by the scale setting on the meter.

To measure current, the meter must be inserted in *series* with the branch to be tested. Figure 6-3 demonstrates the proper connections to measure current in a circuit branch. From the figure, it can be seen that all of the circuit current is put through the meter with this hookup. To protect the coil, a resistor is placed in parallel with the coil and conducts most of the current. This is called a shunt resistor and its resistance is changed by the scale of the meter, just like the dropping resistor in the voltmeter. Figure 6-4 shows this shunt resistor and the connections for a common current meter.

When measuring current and voltage, the meter has no internal power supply and depends on the circuit it is measuring to supply the current necessary to operate the coil. Consequently, these readings must

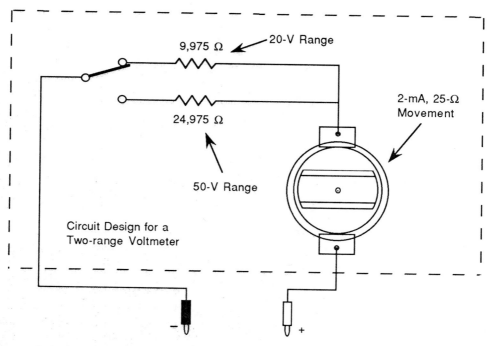

Figure 6-2   Inside an Analog Voltmeter

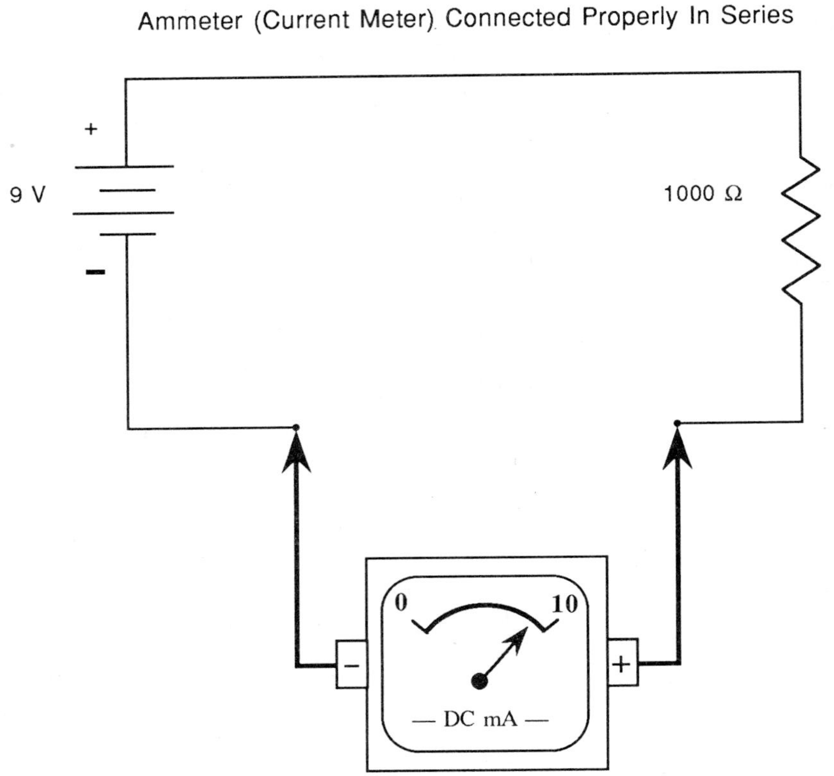

Ammeter (Current Meter) Connected Properly In Series

Figure 6-3   Current Meter Connection

be taken with the circuit energized (turned on). This means that to prevent meter damage or personal injury, much care should be taken to connect the meter properly and to have the meter set on on the proper scale. If there is any question about the voltage or current to be measured, turn the circuit off, insert the meter set on the highest scale available on the meter, and then turn the circuit on. If a different scale is needed, change the scale settings one at a time until the proper reading is obtained. This will prevent meter burnout or explosion due to excess current or voltage.

To measure resistance, the circuit must be de-energized (turned off). If voltage is applied to the ohmmeter, it will be damaged and will be in need of repair or replacement. The power required for resistance measurements is provided by an internal battery, usually 1.5 V or 9 V. Figure 6-5 shows the proper connection of an ohmmeter in a simple circuit. Figure

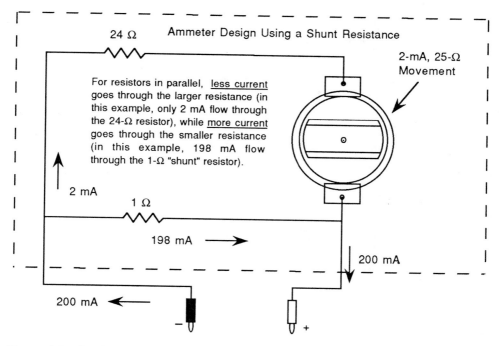

Figure 6-4   Inside a Current Meter

6-6 displays the internal circuitry of the ohmmeter, showing the battery and a series resistor to protect the coil.

Much care should be used to isolate the circuit under inspection when taking resistance measurements, or the reading obtained will not be of the intended circuit or component. Figure 6-7 illustrates the problem of parallel paths that can easily be encountered when trying to measure resistance of components still connected in the circuit.

Now that you know something about the operation of these meters, look at Figure 6-8, which shows several types of common multimeters.

Other Meters

There are several other types of meters. Most are built for a specific purpose and are named for what they measure. A powermeter or wattmeter measures power consumption (watts) and is usually hooked to the output

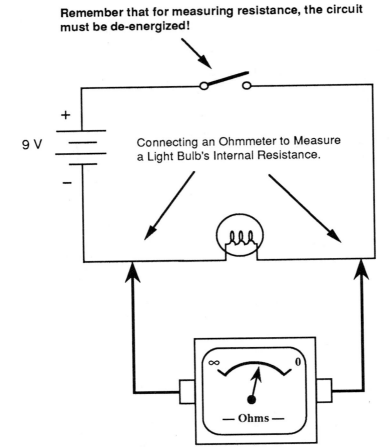

Remember that for measuring resistance, the circuit must be de-energized!

9 V

+

−

Connecting an Ohmmeter to Measure a Light Bulb's Internal Resistance.

∞   0

— Ohms —

Figure 6-5   Ohmmeter Connection

of a transmitter or power device. Wattmeters are commonly found on high-power stereo amplifiers to monitor the power output.

A megger is a specialized type of ohmmeter. It is used for measuring very high resistances that are out of the range of ordinary meters.

Other types of special meters have been developed to perform very specific tasks. The transistor checker is a meter that checks the type and quality of semiconductor devices. The capacitor checker performs a similar function for capacitors.

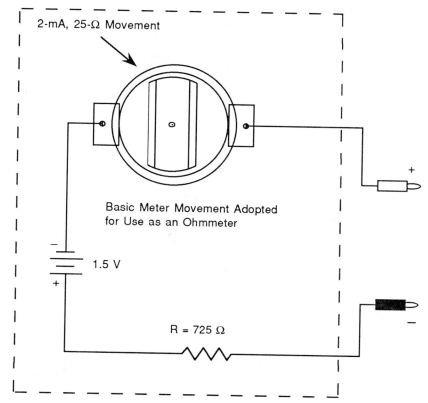

Figure 6-6   Inside an Ohmmeter

Oscilloscopes

An oscilloscope is a device that allows us to see electrical waveforms (like the ones discussed earlier in the text) and to measure their parameters. For this reason, the oscilloscope is an indispensable tool of the electronics laboratory. Figure 6-9 is a picture of a typical oscilloscope.

When connected in the circuit, an oscilloscope will display a graph of voltage versus time. Time is displayed along the horizontal axis and voltage magnitude along the vertical. If a scope (as it is commonly called) is attached to an AC source, as shown in Figure 6-9, a sine wave can be displayed and analyzed. The voltage scale and the time scale are both variable to provide for the display of various signals. The screen is equipped with a scaled grid that can be used in conjunction with the

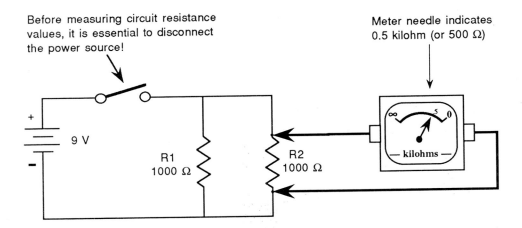

Before measuring circuit resistance
values, it is essential to disconnect
the power source!

Meter needle indicates
0.5 kilohm (or 500 Ω)

As illustrated in this example, instead of indicating 1000 Ω of resistance as
the value of R2, the ohmmeter will indicate the 500 Ω equivalent parallel
resistance of R1 with R2, that it is actually measuring.

Figure 6-7   Circuit Problems When Checking Resistance

voltage and time scale controls to measure the parameters of the displayed waveform.

POWER SUPPLIES

Power supplies are generally thought of as devices that run on AC voltage
and produce DC voltage. The half-wave and full-wave rectifiers discussed
earlier are power supplies, but their outputs are very bumpy, as you may
recall. Special circuits used to smooth out these bumps are explained in
the next section.

Power supplies are built to the requirements of the circuit to be pow-
ered, unless they are designated for general use. Power supplies are rated
by their current- and voltage-producing capabilities and must be able to
dissipate the heat generated by the conversion of voltages.

The most common type of rectifier used in power supplies is the
full-wave bridge. Figure 6-10 shows a bridge rectifier with typical input
and output waveforms. This type of rectifier is used because it is the most
efficient and makes the best use of the diodes. Let's trace the current paths
through the diodes while they are conducting. Figure 6-11 shows the cur-

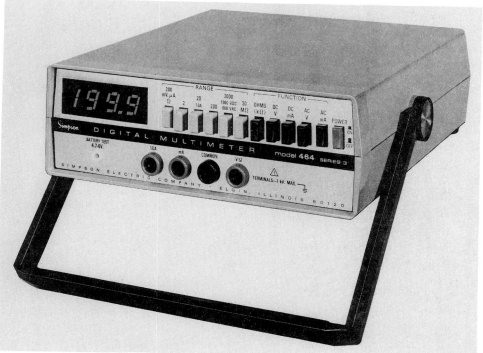

Figure 6-8   Common Multimeters: a) Analog Multimeter; b) Hand-held Multimeter; c) Bench-top Multimeter (Courtesy of Simpson Electric Co., Elgin, IL)

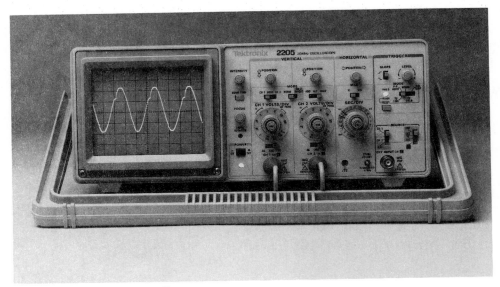

Figure 6-9   A Typical Oscilloscope

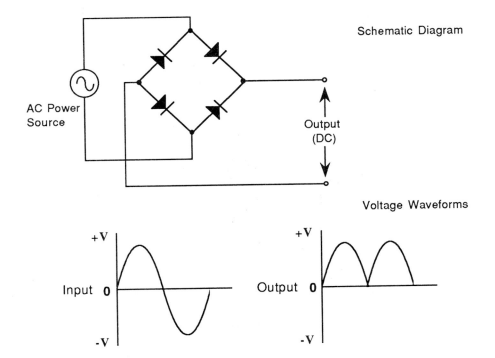

Figure 6-10   A Full-wave Bridge Rectifier

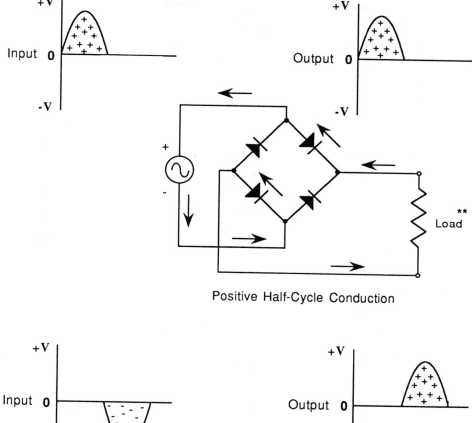

Positive Half-Cycle Conduction

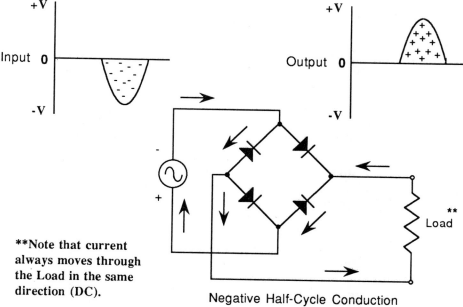

**Note that current always moves through the Load in the same direction (DC).

Negative Half-Cycle Conduction

Figure 6-11   Bridge Rectifier Current Paths

Capacitors resist changes in voltage. Consequently, this filter configuration opposes voltage changes.

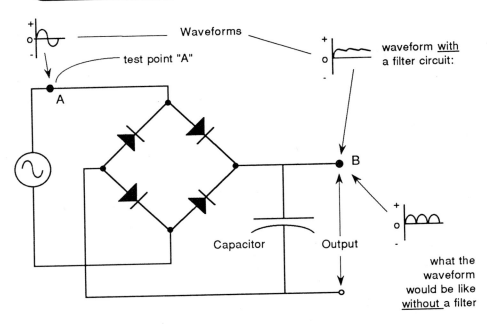

Figure 6-12   Capacitor Filter Action

rent paths on the positive and negative half-cycles of the AC input and demonstrates the rectifier action.

From the figures it can be seen that the current flow through the output terminals is in the same direction, regardless of the polarity of the input. This fulfills the definition of rectification.

FILTERS AND REGULATION

Filters smooth the bumps out of the DC waveform. Remember that inductors oppose a change in current and capacitors oppose a change in voltage. The same principles are used to construct filters. If a capacitor is connected between a rectifier's output leads, it will smooth out the bumps

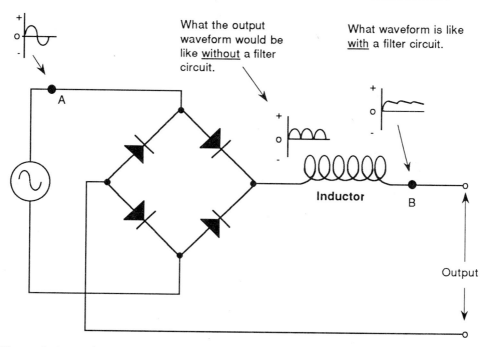

Inductors resist changes in current. Consequently, this filter configuration <u>opposes current changes</u>.

What the output waveform would be like <u>without</u> a filter circuit.

What waveform is like <u>with</u> a filter circuit.

A

Inductor   B

Output

Figure 6-13   Inductor Filter Action

as it charges and discharges with the changing voltage amplitude. Figure 6-12 shows a rectifier with a single filter capacitor and waveforms at three places so that the effects of the components are more clear.

Inductors have a similar smoothing action when they are inserted in series with the output current. Figure 6-13 shows a typical inductor filtering action with representative waveforms.

Generally, the more capacitance and/or inductance added to the bridge output, the smoother the resulting voltage will be. If the components are combined in a circuit, the filtering action is also combined and the DC becomes very smooth. Figure 6-14 shows a typical filter and the significant filtering that has taken place. The resultant DC is very stable and can be used in most applications.

> This type of filter is sometimes referred to as a pi filter because it resembles "π." It <u>opposes changes in both current and voltage.</u>

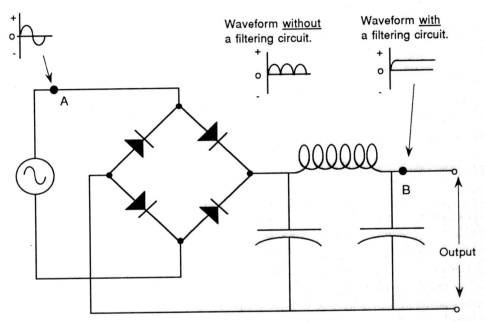

Waveform <u>without</u> a filtering circuit.

Waveform <u>with</u> a filtering circuit.

Figure 6-14   Typical Filtering Action

MOTORS AND GENERATORS

Motors and generators are included here because they are essentially inductors and magnetic fields in action. They are also fundamental devices in electricity and electronics. The basic difference between electric motors and generators is that motors produce mechanical energy from electrical energy, while generators produce electrical energy from mechanical energy. The major parts of the motor are the case, the field windings, the rotor, and the shaft with its bearings. Many motor types are also required to have a way of connecting the rotating loop residing on the rotor with stationary terminals, connected to external circuitry. Brushes and a commutator (DC machine) or slip rings (AC machine) are used for this purpose.

In an AC motor, the AC voltage is applied to the field, or stator, windings. An electromagnetic field is generated by the stator windings, and as it expands it induces a voltage in the rotating loop on the rotor. The windings of the rotor are made of heavy, single-loop, low-resistance, copper wires, allowing for large currents to flow around the loops. Those currents produce a magnetic field in the rotor which will cause it to follow the stator field as it rotates and therefore turn with it. In other words, the rotor is constantly being pushed by the moving field of the stator.

With a DC motor, the process is a little more complicated. The stator field in this type of motor remains unchanged. It is generated by either an electromagnet or a permanent magnet. Most common DC motor types have a commutator mounted to the shaft. Generally, the commutator converts an AC machine for use with a DC voltage. It enables the DC machine to produce torque in one direction by constantly relocating the field of the rotor to keep ahead of the stator field. This way the forces produced by the interaction of the two fields create the necessary torque to run the motor. Blenders, drill motors, and fan motors in heating and air conditioning units are examples of this type.

Generators are quite similar to motors; in fact, a generator can be made by taking some types of motors and spinning the shaft manually. When this is done, a voltage is produced that can be measured at the input leads. Generators are usually connected to some type of mechanical system that provides for the rotation of the shaft. Sometimes a small gas engine is used, as in many portable generators. Hydroelectric power plants use falling water to turn the blades of a turbine which, in turn, rotates the shaft. The generator in a car uses the auto's engine for power which is transmitted through a belt and pulley system.

Motors and generators have a large impact on our standard of living. More information on motors and generators can be found in most electrical applications manuals.

CHAPTER REVIEW

On a separate sheet of paper, write a response to each question, statement, or problem below.

Short Answer

1. Briefly describe how an analog voltmeter works.
2. To measure the resistance in a circuit with an ohmmeter, why must the circuit be de-energized?
3. What is an oscilloscope used for?
4. What is the purpose of a power supply?
5. Why are filters used in circuits?
6. What is the basic difference between a motor and a generator?
7. Describe how a motor operates.
8. Explain the operation of a generator.

7

Diodes

INTRODUCTION

From the electronic alarm clock to the telephone, from digital thermostats to electronic watches, from microwave ovens to televisions, diodes are everywhere. Although this chapter on diodes may at first seem difficult, the importance of these tiny devices to electronics makes your study of them worth the effort.

CONSTRUCTION AND OPERATION

A pure semiconductor is a material that is neither a good conductor nor a good insulator. The most common semiconductors are made of silicon and germanium. A good semiconductor must be lightly contaminated with an impurity that makes the resultant mixture either overpopulated with electrons (a negatively charged N-type material) or underpopulated with electrons (a positively charged P-type material). This contamination process is called doping. If a P-type material is connected to an N-type material, the result is a P-N junction. This junction, illustrated in Figure 7-1, is the basis for all common diodes, transistors, and other semiconductor components.

At the junction, a recombination of negative charges (electrons) from the N-type material and positive charges (holes) from the P-type material occurs and forms a small area called the depletion zone, as shown in Figure 7-2a. The width of this depletion zone determines the conduction characteristics of the diode. If a negative voltage is applied to the N-type material and a positive voltage is applied to the P-type material, the diode is said to be forward biased. This condition, shown in Figure 7-2b, causes the width of the depletion zone to narrow and allows current to flow through the diode. If the applied voltages are reversed, as in Figure 7-2c,

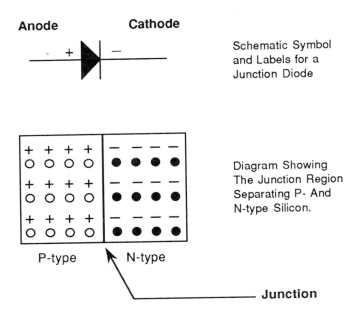

Figure 7-1   Diode Construction

the diode is reverse biased. This causes the depletion zone to widen and present great resistance to current flow.

Simply stated, the diode allows current flow only when it is forward biased. However, when a diode is forward biased, current does not flow immediately. A small voltage must be applied to overcome the resistance of the depletion zone. This is called the barrier potential and is the voltage drop across a conducting diode. Also, there is a small current, called leakage current, that flows when the diode is reverse biased. Every diode has a specific reverse-bias voltage, called the breakdown voltage, at which it will conduct in the reverse direction. When this breakdown voltage is exceeded, a large reverse current occurs and the diode is usually destroyed.

Figure 7-3 is a conduction curve for a common diode. It can be seen from Figure 7-3 that the current curve extends upward and downward in almost a straight line, indicating that current conduction is unlimited. This is not true, however, as each diode has a maximum current value (Imax) which, if exceeded, usually causes the destruction of the diode. Maximum current and maximum reverse voltage must be taken into consideration when designing circuits; the operating range of the diode must stay within these limits if the diode is to survive.

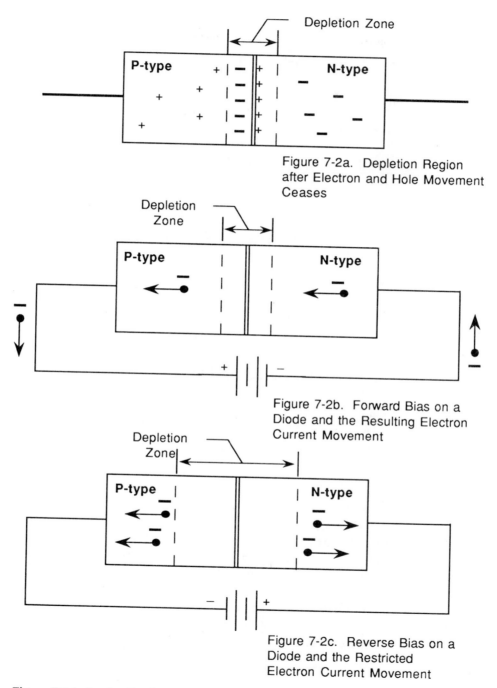

Figure 7-2a. Depletion Region after Electron and Hole Movement Ceases

Figure 7-2b. Forward Bias on a Diode and the Resulting Electron Current Movement

Figure 7-2c. Reverse Bias on a Diode and the Restricted Electron Current Movement

Figure 7-2 (a, b, c) Diode Biasing and the Depletion Zone

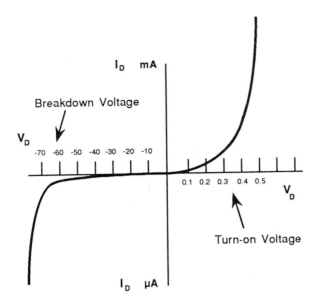

Figure 7-3   The Diode Conduction Curve

Figure 7-4 shows the schematic symbol for a standard P-N junction diode and indicates the direction of current flow in forward- and reverse-biased situations.

SPECIAL DIODES

The most common type of special diode is the zener diode. The zener is constructed so that the reverse voltage conduction point is controllable. The zener is designed to operate normally in this reverse-biased condition. Zeners are available at many voltage ratings and are generally used as voltage regulators or limiters. Figure 7-5 shows the typical operating curve for a zener diode. Because zeners are intended to operate in this reverse-biased region, they are placed in the circuit backwards, compared to the conventional diode. Consideration must be given to current limiting in the zener circuit, just as in the conventional diode circuit. Figure 7-6 is a typical zener application.

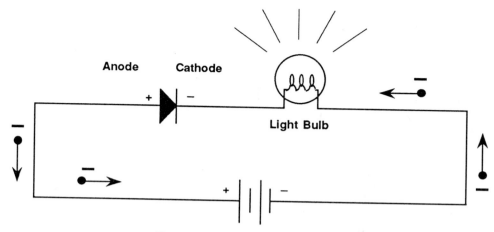

Figure 7-4a. In this circuit, Forward Bias on the Diode will enable current to flow, and the light bulb will be illuminated.

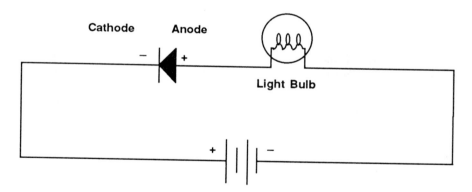

Figure 7-4b. For this circuit, Reverse Bias on the Diode will <u>prevent</u> current from flowing, and the light bulb will <u>not</u> be illuminated.

Figure 7-4 (a, b)   Diode Symbols and Current Direction

The silicon-controlled rectifier (SCR) is another type of specialized diode found in common use. A power rectifier used extensively in industrial control circuits, it is essentially a diode with an extra input used to control its conduction. In an SCR, conduction does not depend on a forward-bias voltage across its main leads. Instead, to control the start of

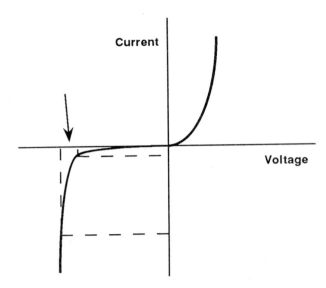

Figure 7-5   Zener Conduction Curve

conduction, a third lead, called the gate, is used. Figure 7-7 shows the SCR schematic diagram and basic operation.

The major benefit of the SCR is that it allows large currents and voltages to be controlled with small bias voltages. It is not unusual to find SCRs that conduct currents in the hundreds of amps, controlled by a signal less than 10 V and 0.05 A.

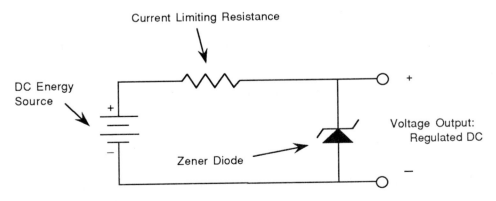

Figure 7-6   A Zener as a Voltage Regulator

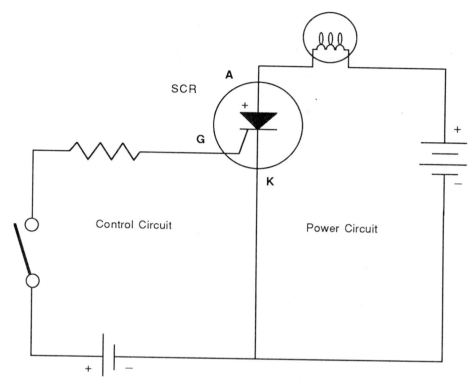

Figure 7-7 The SCR

A second cousin to the SCR is the triac. Like the SCR, the triac's conduction is controlled by applying a voltage (signal) to the gate, but the triac itself is like two diodes hooked up in opposite directions. It allows a small DC voltage to control an AC voltage. The triac has many applications where DC circuits control AC devices, such as in lights, fan motors, thermostats, etc. Figure 7-8 shows the triac's symbol and a typical application.

The last common type of diode to be discussed is the light-emitting diode (LED). The LED gives off either visible or infrared light when it is forward biased. It uses small amounts of current, has a long life expectancy, fast switching times, and is inexpensive. LEDs commonly turn on at 1 to 3 V and draw 0.02 to 0.2 A. They are commonly used for digital displays, indicator lights, and remote controls (infrared). Figure 7-9 provides the schematic symbol and a common circuit for the LED.

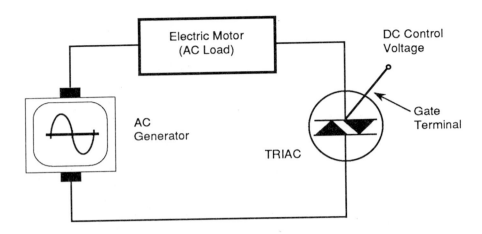

When the DC control voltage magnitude exceeds
the gate's trigger level, the AC motor will be turned on.

Figure 7-8   The Triac

Figure 7-10 is a block diagram with waveforms to show the signals
as they progress through a common regulated power supply. It is a combination of several of the circuits that we have looked at in this chapter.

There has always been some disagreement about the dividing line
between electricity and electronics. The circuits that have been studied in
the previous six chapters can be argued to be on either side of the line,

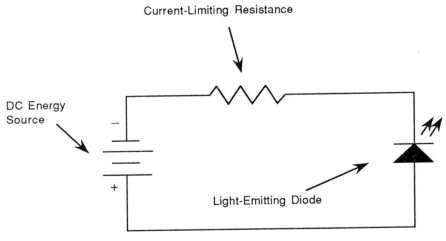

Figure 7-9   The LED

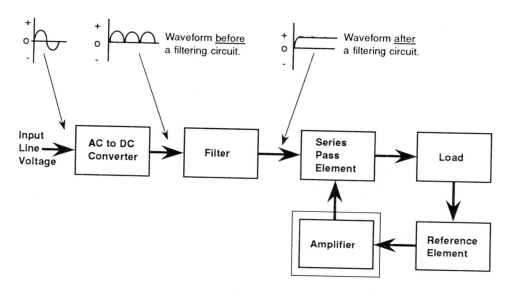

This block diagram represents a form of series regulated power supply. The first two blocks are the familiar elements of a basic unregulated power supply (previously illustrated by Figures 6-12 through 6-16). In this circuit, the series pass element is the control element—the element that turns the "electron valve" up and down to maintain a constant voltage at the load, a load that may be changing, or it compensates for changes in the input line voltage.

The series pass element is normally a power transistor performing this control function. The reference element is a constant voltage device that compares the output voltage with itself and, when necessary, sends out an "error" signal to the control element. This error signal is passed on to an amplifier, which then relays it to the series pass element.

Figure 7-10 Block Diagram of a Regulated Power Supply

but when the circuits include diodes or any of the more complex components, they are generally accepted to be part of electronics.

Before solid-state electronics came into being, diodes were vacuum tubes; indeed, the first vacuum tube was a diode. These vacuum tube diodes found widespread use for many years and served their purpose well, but the development of the semiconductor marked the end of the vacuum tube era. Vacuum tube and semiconductor diodes perform the same function but their operation is considerably different.

CHAPTER REVIEW

On a separate sheet of paper, write a response to each question, statement, or problem below.

Fill in the Blank

1. An N-type semiconductor is overpopulated with _____ while a P-type semiconductor is overpopulated with _____.

2. In forward bias, a _____ voltage is applied to the N-type material and a _____ voltage is applied to the P-type material.

3. With reverse bias, a negative voltage is applied to the ____type material and a positive voltage is applied to the ____type material.

4. The voltage at which a diode will start conducting in the reverse condition is called the _____ _____.

5. The zener diode is used as a _____.

6. With an SCR, a third lead, called the _____, is used to control the start of conduction.

7. An LED is used for _____, _____, and _____.

Short Answer

1. List typical applications for a triac.

8

Transistors and Their Circuits

INTRODUCTION

From early radio to digital television, the transistor has been the backbone of the electronics field. The transistor, more than any other single development, is responsible for the growth of electronics in the twentieth century.

TRANSISTOR FUNDAMENTALS

The bipolar junction transistor was developed in 1948 and from the start its advantages over vacuum tubes were significant. As transistors improved in the areas of reliability, cost, and current-handling capability, they replaced vacuum tubes in new designs and fabrications. By the late 1950s, transistors were used in most electronic applications. Today there are only a few functions that are still performed by tubes, but transistors and their miniature offspring, integrated circuits, are threatening complete domination.

Transistors are called solid-state devices because the electron flow is through a solid material (semiconductor). Vacuum tubes, on the other hand, use thermionic emission (free electrons emitted into a vacuum) as their means of current flow. At first glance, a transistor looks like a double-ended diode. It is constructed of three sections of doped semiconductor material and arranged in either a PNP or an NPN order.

Figure 8-1 includes a transistor construction pictorial and schematic symbols. The emitter, as its name implies, is the starting point for electrical charges that travel through the device. The base is a thin strip of material that controls the amount of conduction. The collector also performs as its name indicates. It is the "catcher's mitt" for the electrical charges as they flow through the transistor.

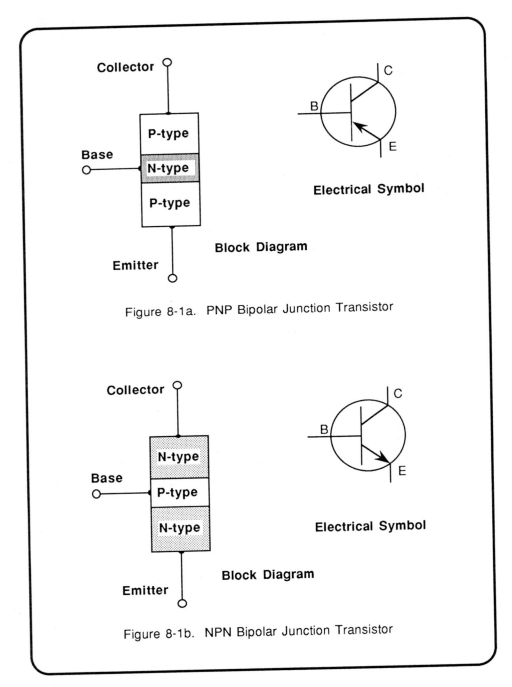

Figure 8-1a. PNP Bipolar Junction Transistor

Figure 8-1b. NPN Bipolar Junction Transistor

Figure 8-1   Transistor Construction and Symbols

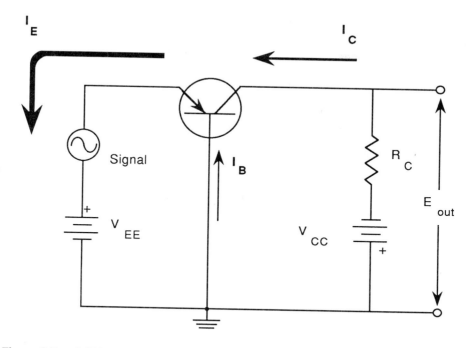

Figure 8-2   A PNP Transistor Properly Biased to Act as a Basic Amplifier

Figure 8-2 illustrates the biasing that is required for conduction and the currents that flow as a result of proper biasing. It is important to note that, for a transistor to function normally, the emitter-base junction must be forward biased and the base-collector junction must be reverse biased.

Several other observations can be made about Figure 8-2. The size of the current arrows is indicative of the magnitude of the currents. The emitter current (IE) is 100 percent of the current through the transistor. When the current gets to the base, it splits. Approximately 98 percent of the emitter current becomes collector current (IC) and the other 2 percent becomes base current (IB). Even though the base current is small, it is important because the bias voltage on the base determines the conduction of the transistor. This will be discussed further in the next section.

AMPLIFIERS: GAIN AND FEEDBACK

Transistors are most commonly used as amplifiers; that is, they can produce a large output signal from a small input signal or a large current

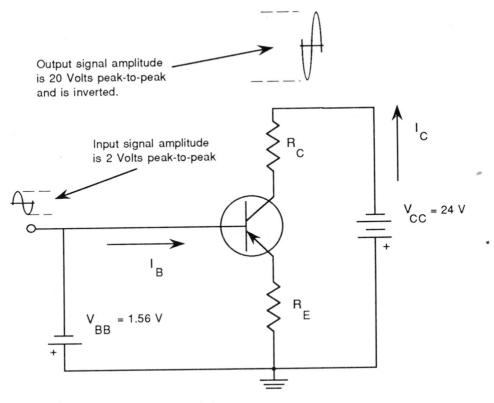

Figure 8-3   A Typical Transistor Amplifier

from a small current. The ratio of the output signal to the input signal is called gain. If the input is 2 volts and the output is 40 volts, the gain is 20. The same principles apply to current.

Transistors amplify because they are connected in such a way that a small input signal applied across the base and emitter causes a large change in the voltage across the collector and emitter. Accordingly, a small change in the base current produces a large change in the current flowing through the collector. Figure 8-3 shows a diagram of a transistor amplifier circuit with the input and output signals. Notice that since the input voltage causes a change in the voltage at the output, the output voltage can never exceed the collector supply voltage (Vcc).

The two important things to notice are that the input and output signals are going high and low at opposite times but the crossover points occur at the same times. This means that the signals have the same frequency but they are out of phase. In some circuits, when the input goes

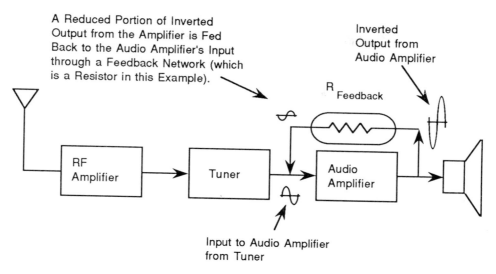

Figure 8-4   The Use of Feedback

up, the output also goes up. In these circuits the input and output are said to be in phase. This phase relationship must be anticipated and designed into the circuit but normally causes no great problems. The next section will show us which amplifiers invert the input signal and which ones do not.

Control of the amplifier is a major concern when designing circuits. One way to control the output is to carefully monitor the input and change it as necessary. A common method for amplifier control is the use of feedback. Feedback is the use of the output signal in such a way that it constantly adjusts the input signal so that the proper output is obtained. Figure 8-4 is a block diagram of a feedback loop that is commonly used in audio circuits of radios.

Feedback can either increase or decrease the output signal. When the feedback is in phase with the input, it is called positive feedback. When it is out of phase with the input, it counteracts the input and is called negative feedback. The type that is required depends on the circuit application. If the purpose of the circuit is to regulate the output of a speaker to a constant sound level (as in Figure 8-4), negative feedback is used to limit the output to a desirable level. If, however, the purpose of the circuit is maximum output, positive feedback is used to enhance the input signal.

A transistor amplifier can be biased so that it reproduces all or part of the input signal, as desired. There are three classes of amplification that

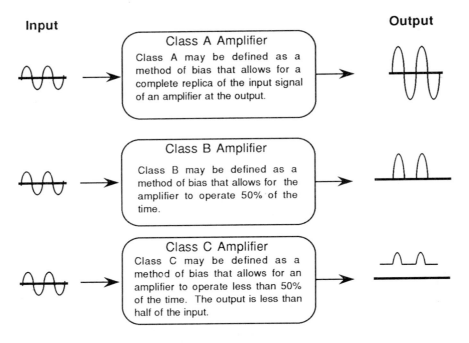

Figure 8-5   Classes of Amplifiers

describe the relationship between the input and output signals of the amplifier. Figure 8-5 shows the inputs and outputs of these circuits.

Class A amplifiers are used to amplify and reproduce the input signal as accurately as possible. Distortion is held to a minimum by biasing the transistor so that any change in the input can cause a change in the output. Class B amplifiers generate distortion by clipping off some of the input waveform; however, because the distorted signal can easily be repaired, the efficiency gained is worth the distortion incurred. Class C has the highest amount of distortion but is the most efficient type of amplifier.

TRANSISTOR CONFIGURATIONS

There are three ways to connect a transistor into a circuit. These different hookups are called circuit configurations. The names for these configurations are common emitter, common base, and common collector. The "common" refers to the connection that is used in both the input and output circuits. Figure 8-6 shows all three configurations and their circuitry.

Table 8-6a

Input and Output Signal Relations of a Common-Emitter Circuit

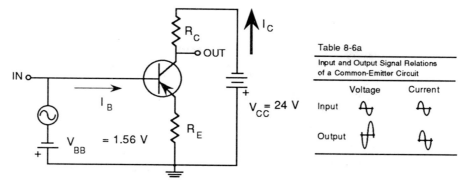

Figure 8-6a Common-Emitter Configuration

Table 8-6b

Input and Output Signal Relations of a Common-Base Circuit

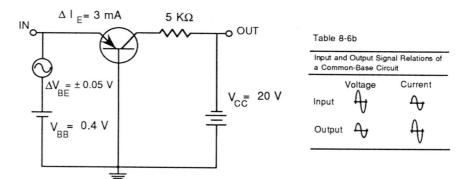

Figure 8-6b Common-Base Configuration

Table 8-6c

Input and Output Signal Relations of a Common-Collector Circuit

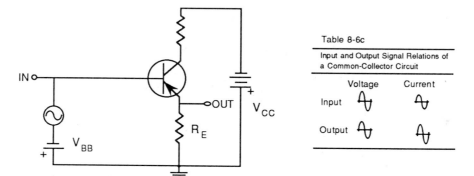

Figure 8-6c Common-Collector Configuration

Figure 8-6 Amplifier Configurations

Table 8-1   Amplifier Input/Output Characteristics

	Common-emitter	*Common-collector*	*Common-base*
Voltage gain	High	Low	High
Maximum current gain	High	High	Low
Power gain	Very high	High	High
Input Impedance	Low	High	Very low
Output Impedance	High	Very low	High

The obvious question raised by Figure 8-6 concerns the differences between these circuits. Table 8-1 shows the type of configuration, the current gain, the voltage gain, the power gain, and whether or not the circuit inverts the input signal. These characteristics are of great importance to the circuit designer.

Before we leave our discussion of transistors, a special type of transistor should be introduced: the FET (field effect transistor). The FET performs like a regular transistor, but it has several significant differences. It is smaller than its bipolar cousin and has characteristics that make it the common choice in miniature, low-power circuits. It also has a very high input impedance, very high gain, and is less sensitive to temperature, X-rays, and cosmic radiation. These differences make it very useful in some cases and unusable in others. As FETs become more developed, they will also become more practical and popular.

SPECIALIZED CIRCUITS

Now that you have some knowledge about transistors and how they work, we will see some special circuits that perform specific tasks. All of these circuits use transistors in some way.

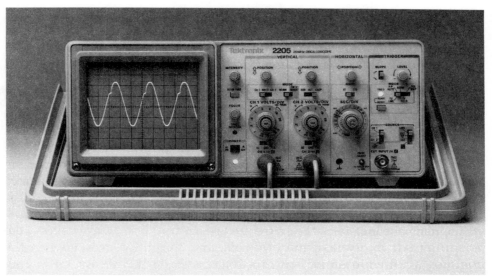

Figure 8-7   Oscillator Output Waveform

The oscillator is one of the most common circuits. It is a DC-powered circuit that produces a sine-wave. The frequency of the oscillator is controlled by the components in the circuit. An oscillator usually uses a transistor as an amplifier, and an inductor/capacitor tank circuit. The tank circuit is what causes the oscillations; it is tuned to operate at a certain frequency (the frequency of the oscillator). Nevertheless, it cannot sustain oscillation without an external source of energy. For this reason, the tank circuit is connected to the transistor amplifier output, and feedback is applied to its input through a capacitor to synchronize it with the oscillating frequency. Figure 8-7 shows the output of a typical oscillator.

Another common type of circuit is the multivibrator. There are three basic types of multivibrators: the astable, the monostable, and the bistable. All multivibrators, except the astable, require an input to function. The astable multivibrator switches back and forth between states on its own, producing a square wave output. It is essentially a square wave oscillator.

The monostable has only one stable state. An input pulse flips it to its unstable state for a certain period of time, determined by the circuitry. Once this predetermined period of time expires, it switches back to its stable state. The bistable, which is also commonly referred to as flip-flop, has two stable states. It will stay in the same state until it receives an input pulse to flip to the other state. The flip-flop will remain in its new state until another pulse causes it to change.

BASIC AM AND FM RADIOS

Before we study these two basic wireless communication techniques, we need to discuss two processes essential to their operation: modulation and heterodyning. Modulation is the process of varying a frequency component called a carrier with the instantaneous value of another frequency (the modulation frequency). The two types of modulation used most frequently are amplitude modulation (AM) and frequency modulation (FM). In AM, the amplitude, or height of the carrier wave, is modulated with the audio frequency from the microphone, as shown in Figure 8-8. In FM, as you would expect, the frequency of the carrier is varied by the audio signal, as demonstrated in Figure 8-9.

Heterodyning is the process of combining two frequencies to generate two new frequencies. Four frequencies result from this process: the two originals, the sum of the originals, and the difference between the originals, as illustrated in Figure 8-10. Heterodyning allows us to mix frequencies together and select the output frequency that best suits our purpose. All of the information that was contained in the original carriers

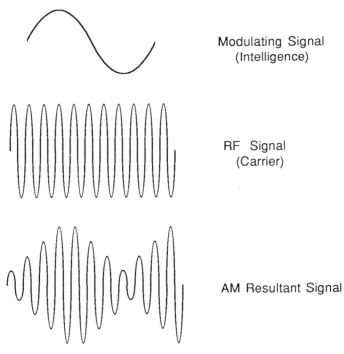

Modulating Signal
(Intelligence)

RF Signal
(Carrier)

AM Resultant Signal

Figure 8-8   Amplitude Modulation (AM)

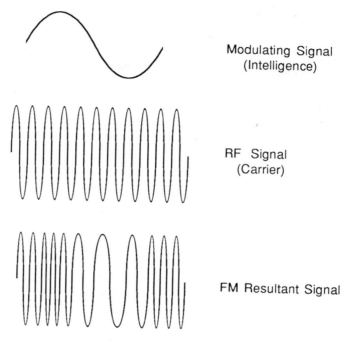

Figure 8-9   Frequency Modulation (FM)

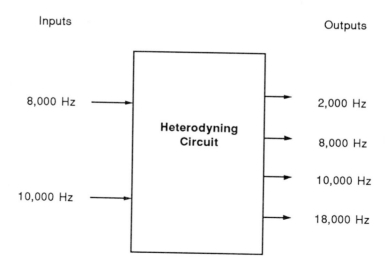

The Outputs are the Sum, the Difference, and the
Two Original Frequencies.

Figure 8-10   Heterodyning

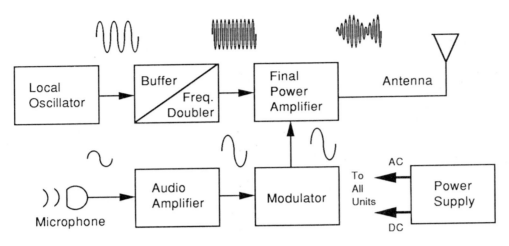

Figure 8-11　A Typical AM Transmitter

is still contained in the resultant. The use and importance of both of these principles will become clear as we discuss radio communication.

Figure 8-11 shows a typical AM transmitter block diagram. Notice how the carrier frequency and the audio frequency are generated separately and mixed in the modulator. The signal then goes to the power amplifier and on to the antenna. Compare this to the AM receiver in Figure 8-12.

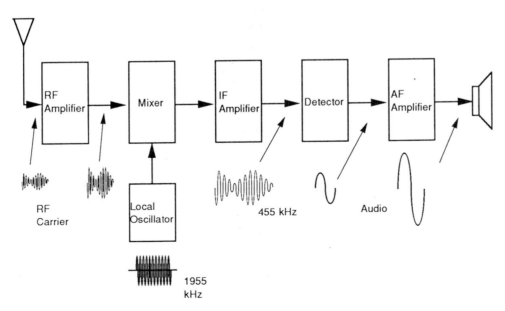

Figure 8-12　A Typical AM Receiver

The extra parts in an AM receiver make it more practical and more sensitive, with better noise rejection. In addition, these extra parts provide more gain and selectivity as well as better tuning and less static. The signal is received by the antenna and goes into the radio frequency (RF) amplifier. Here, the weak carrier signal is amplified. In addition, all frequencies except the carrier (and those near it) are filtered out through the use of frequency-tuned capacitor/inductor circuits. Because these tuned circuits are adjustable, any carrier frequency in the AM band can be selected and amplified.

The next part is a bit more complicated. In the mixer, the received carrier signal and a signal from a local oscillator are mixed together, producing a single output. The frequency of the local oscillator is determined by the setting of the tuner knob on the radio. The tuned circuits in the RF amplifier are also mechanically connected to the same knob so that they are adjusted together. This is done in such a way that the "difference" frequency from the mixer remains unchanged, regardless of the setting of the tuner knob. This is the intermediate frequency, or IF. IF still carries all the information that was modulated on the carrier from the transmitter; but unlike the carrier, whose frequency may vary, its frequency is constant, with a typical value of 455,000 hertz.

The purpose of an IF is to allow all of the radio circuits to be tuned to a fixed frequency, except for the RF section. This provides for maximum sensitivity of the receiver without the problem of having to retune the radio each time the station is changed.

The next part of the circuit is the IF amplifier, which is just what its name implies. It simply increases the amplitude of the signal. Now the signal enters the detector, which separates the IF carrier frequency from the audio frequency and sends the audio signal only to the audio amplifier and then to the speaker.

Now that you have studied each of the circuits in this AM radio and have an understanding of its operation, it is time to move on to the FM method of signal transmission. The block diagrams of the FM transmitter and receiver are no more complicated than those for the AM system but the circuits are a little more complex. Look at the transmitter in Figure 8-13. All of the functions are the same as for the AM transmitter except that, as you know from our earlier discussion of FM, the modulation changes the frequency of the carrier and not its amplitude. From Figure 8-14, you can see that a typical FM receiver differs from an AM receiver in only one respect: the FM discriminator replaces the AM detector.

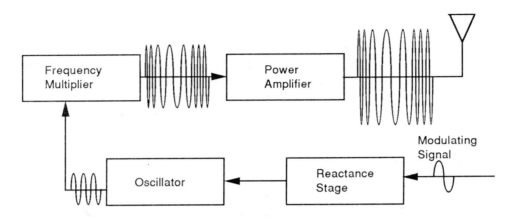

Figure 8-13   A Typical FM Transmitter

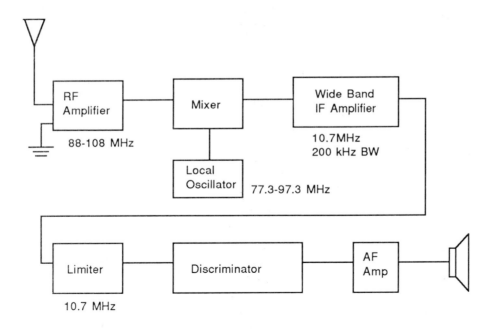

Figure 8-14   A Typical FM Receiver

CHAPTER REVIEW

On a separate sheet of paper, write a response to each question, statement, or problem below.

Short Answer

1. What is the difference between a solid-state diode and a vacuum diode?
2. What are the functions of a transistor's base, emitter, and collector?
3. What is a transistor amplifier? How would you describe its gain?
4. Why might feedback be used in an amplifier circuit?
5. What is the result of using positive feedback, and what is the result of using negative feedback?
6. With respect to distortion and efficiency, how would you compare Class A, Class B, and Class C amplifiers?
7. Briefly describe the three different transistor-amplifier configurations.
8. Discuss how oscillators work and what they might be used for.
9. List the three basic types of multivibrator and distinguish between their outputs.
10. Describe the difference between amplitude modulation (AM) and frequency modulation (FM).

True or False

1. In a transistor, the emitter and collector currents are very large compared to the base current.
2. Feedback is a method of controlling the output signal by using the output signal itself to influence the input signal.
3. When the feedback is out of phase with the input, it is called positive feedback.
4. Class C amplifiers have the least distortion.
5. The astable multivibrator is a square-wave oscillator.
6. A bistable oscillator has only one stable state.
7. With amplitude modulation, the amplitude of the carrier is modulated by the audio signal.
8. Heterodyning is the method of mixing two frequencies.

9

Digital Logic

INTRODUCTION

Digital electronics has developed into its own branch of study and application. Digital systems are circuits and devices that function with only two voltage levels, designated "one" and "zero," as opposed to analog systems, which use a range of voltage levels. The most common application of digital electronics is probably the computer, but more applications will arise as technology advances. There are now digitally controlled fishing reels that prevent "backlash" when casting, programmable thermostats for homes and offices, and computerized lawn sprinklers that allow us to water the grass while we sleep. Automobiles, microwave ovens, videotape recorders, telephones, and televisions are all changing from analog to digital control. Remember the old saying, "Everything's going to plastic by and by"? Well, the new saying might be, "Everything's going to be digital by and by," as all sorts of digital developments affect our lives.

In this first of three chapters on digital electronics and computers, we will discuss the building blocks of digital systems. We will begin by learning several different ways to count, and the logic used to control these number systems. Next, we will look at gates, as some basic logic circuits are called, and find out how they function. Finally, digital circuits and applications will be discussed.

NUMBER SYSTEMS

We are used to base 10 numbers, our decimal system. When we see a base 10 number, we know what it means because of the numbers themselves and their placement. Each column has a value. The first column is the "ones," the second is the "tens," etc. The other systems we are going to look at follow the same format but use different values and symbols.

We will look at three numbering systems that are commonly used in digital systems: base 2, base 8, and base 16. As you will see, all computer number systems have a base of some power of two (two squared, etc.) because the machine itself functions using only two voltage levels (high and low or one and zero, as they are called).

First, let's look at the binary, or base 2, system. As we said earlier, this system has only two symbols, 1 and 0. Just as in the decimal system, when a column is at its highest number, it goes back to zero and the next column is increased by one (called a carry). 0 is the first binary number. 1 is the second. When the "ones" column is full, it goes to zero and the "twos" goes to 1. So the decimal number 2 in binary is 10. Remember, we are not in base 10 now, so don't say ten; say one, zero. If we add one more, we get 11 (not eleven, but one, one). If you know the next number you have the binary system figured out. Add one to 11, and you get 100 (one, zero, zero) or 4 in base 10.

Try these examples. What is decimal 22 in binary? What is 139? What is the decimal number for binary 11011001? If you break the numbers down to their column value, you will not have any trouble.

Here is an example of binary addition:

7	00000111
+ 5	00000101
12	00001100

Use the rules we have discussed and the above example to add these two binary numbers, 11010001 and 10011101. Did you get 101101110? Remember, when a column gets to its highest number, go to zero and carry.

The next commonly used system is base 8, or octal. The octal system uses numbers 0 to 7. When we get to 7, we go to 0 with a carry. So 8 in the decimal system is 10 in the octal. What is decimal 15 in octal? What is 47? What is octal 341 in base 10? Octal is just like binary but with a few more numbers. The octal system is used because a single octal number represents a group of three binary digits. Note that the highest possible number that can be obtained with three binary digits is the same as the highest octal number (111 in binary or 7 in octal).

The hexadecimal system is base 16. That means that there must be symbols for numbers 0 to 15 that use only one column. Because the base 10 system has only ten symbols, 0 to 9, we must adopt new symbols for 10, 11, 12, 13, 14, and 15 that will go in a single column. The symbols that have been chosen are A, B, C, D, E, and F. Thus in hex, the decimal number

10 is A, 11 is B, and 14 is E. If you were a child growing up in a hex society, you would learn to count like this: 1, 2, 3, 4, 5, 6, 7, 8, 9, A, B, C, D, E, F, 10, 11, 12, 13, 14, 15, 16, 17, 18, 19, 1A, 1B, 1C, 1D, 1E, 1F, 20.

Let's practice a little. What is decimal 20 in hex? 14 (one, four) is the answer. A 1 in the 16's column and a 4 in the 1's column (16 + 4) is 20. What is decimal 32 in hex? What would hex 73 be in decimal? This system is a little confusing, but if you think about the values of the columns, it will become clear. HINT: Many people who use hex all the time do not convert numbers from hex directly to decimal. They go to binary and then to decimal. For example, $5A_{(16)} = 01011010_{(2)} = 90_{(10)}$. Using this method, the task becomes much easier. (Programmers' calculators and tables that simplify number system conversions are available to help you.)

LOGIC AND TRUTH TABLES

As we said earlier, digital machines perform all operations with two voltage levels, 1 and 0. To understand something about how these operations are carried out, we will look at different types of devices used in digital logic circuits. The devices themselves will be described in the next part of this chapter, but now we will discuss what they have in common.

All of these devices have inputs and outputs. These are lines or wires used by the signals to enter and exit the device. As with any type of electronic circuit, the inputs determine the outputs. Since we are dealing with 1's and 0's, the output of any logic device can only be high or low. Each device functions in its own special way and performs a specific function. The relationship between the inputs and the outputs for any given digital circuit can be seen by looking at its truth table. A truth table is a list of all of the possible combinations of inputs and their respective outputs for a particular device. Figure 9-1 shows a typical truth table for a device with 3 inputs and 1 output.

Logic in digital circuits refers to the relationship between the input and output. There are several groups of digital devices that are classified by their general operation and function. Gates, flip-flops, decoders, memories, and microprocessors are some of the main groups. These will be described in the following section. For now, we are concerned only with the fact that they are all high-speed manipulators of 1's and 0's.

Computer designers must be able to combine these circuits to produce the desired results. They must know what each device does and how it works so they know when to use it.

Inputs			Output
I1	I2	I3	
0	0	0	0
0	0	1	1
0	1	0	1
0	1	1	1
1	0	0	1
1	0	1	1
1	1	0	1
1	1	1	1

Figure 9-1   Truth Table for a Three-input Device

GATES AND DEVICES

The inverter, as its name implies, performs a basic logic function called inversion or complementation. This means that the inverter converts one logic level to the other logic level. If the logic level in the input is 0, the output will have a value of 1, and vice-versa. Figure 9-2 shows an inverter. The little circle or "bubble" at the output deserves some explanation. It is called a negation indicator and its presence or absence determines the active state of a line. Its presence indicates that when the output of the device is active it will have a value of 0. Accordingly, absence of the bubble indicates an active 1. Without a bubble the active state of the output is high, and with a bubble the active state is low. That is the way we will refer to the states from now on, as active or inactive, rather than high or low. This concept will become more clear to you later in this section.

The next basic building block of digital logic is the digital switch, or gate, as it is known. There are several types of gates and each is classified by its function. An AND gate can have two or more inputs but only one output. An AND gate operates in such a way that the output will be high only when all of the inputs are high. Look at the AND gate in Figure 9-3. If inputs A, B, and C are high, the output will be high. If one of the inputs is low, the output will be low. Notice the truth table for the AND gate in the figure. It shows the output for any combination of the inputs.

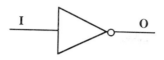

Input (I)	Output (O)
1	0
0	1

Figure 9-2   The Inverter and Its Truth Table

The NAND gate (NAND means not AND) is just like the AND gate except that it has a bubble in the output line. You already know from the inverter that the circle or bubble means that the output is inverted (the opposite of the AND gate), low instead of high and high instead of low. When all inputs are high, the NAND gate will output a low (active). If one or more inputs are low, the output will be high (inactive). Figure 9-4 shows a three-input NAND gate and its truth table.

The OR gate does as it sounds. If either of the inputs is active (A, B, or C), the output will be active. Of course, if more than one or even all of the inputs are active, the output will still be active; the only time that the output is inactive is when all inputs are inactive. From this you should be able to figure out what a NOR gate is. Figure 9-5 shows an OR and a NOR gate and their respective truth tables.

The next two gates to be discussed are great data comparators; that is, they are good at comparing bits. A bit is the smallest amount of digital data possible, a single 1 or 0. These gates are called the exclusive-OR and the exclusive-NOR. The exclusive-OR gate has high output when its inputs have different logic levels. The output is low when the inputs are either all high or all low. The exclusive-NOR has a low output when the inputs have different levels and a high output when the inputs have the same levels. Figure 9-6 shows these two gates and their truth tables.

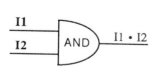

Inputs		Output
I1	I2	I1 • I2
0	0	0
0	1	0
1	0	0
1	1	1

Figure 9-3   The AND Gate and Its Truth Table

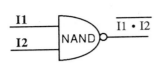

Inputs		Output
I1	I2	$\overline{I1 \cdot I2}$
0	0	1
0	1	1
1	0	1
1	1	0

Figure 9-4   The NAND Gate and Its Truth Table

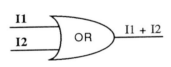

Inputs		Output
I1	I2	$I1 + I2$
0	0	0
0	1	1
1	0	1
1	1	1

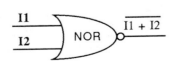

Inputs		Output
I1	I2	$\overline{I1 + I2}$
0	0	1
0	1	0
1	0	0
1	1	0

Figure 9-5   OR and NOR Gates with Truth Tables

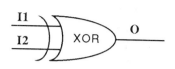

Inputs		Output
I1	I2	O
0	0	0
0	1	1
1	0	1
1	1	0

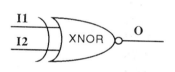

Inputs		Output
I1	I2	O
0	0	1
0	1	0
1	0	0
1	1	1

Figure 9-6   Exclusive Gates and Their Truth Tables

Looking at their truth tables, you can see why they make good data comparators. What matters is not if the inputs are active or inactive but whether they are the same.

Buffers are another type of logic circuit device. Unlike gates, buffers are not decision makers. They have only one input and one output, but some of them have a control, or enable, attached to them. A basic buffer, as shown in Figure 9-7, is just an amplifier. It allows for isolation between circuits and amplification of a signal if it gets too small. You may notice that the buffer looks identical to an inverter, except that it does not have a bubble. This is not a coincidence, since most inverters are also buffers. The truth table shows why it is an inverter.

Figure 9-8 shows the same buffers with an enable line. These are called tri-state buffers. When the control line is active, the same truth table applies, as with the regular buffer. When the enable is inactive, the

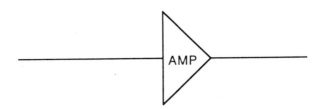

Figure 9-7   The Buffer Amplifier

output is neither a high nor a low but goes to a high impedance state and has no effect on the circuits to which it is connected. This is called tri-state logic; it is used to hook several outputs to one input. Normally, connecting outputs together results in destroying circuits, but with tri-state logic, several outputs can be connected to one input as long as they are turned on only one at a time. That means that only one enable line can be active at any one time, as shown in Figure 9-9.

The next group of devices we will look at are flip-flops. Flip-flops are circuits that have several inputs and two outputs. There are many kinds of flip-flops but a basic flip-flop has two inputs and two outputs. Figure

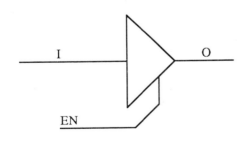

Inputs		Output
I	EN	O
0	1	0
1	1	1.
X	0	HiZ

"X" denotes "Don't Care."

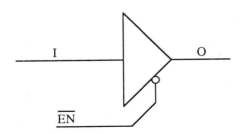

Inputs		Output
I	$\overline{EN}$	O
0	0	0
1	0	1
X	1	HiZ

"X" denotes "Don't Care."

Figure 9-8   Tri-state Buffers and Truth Tables

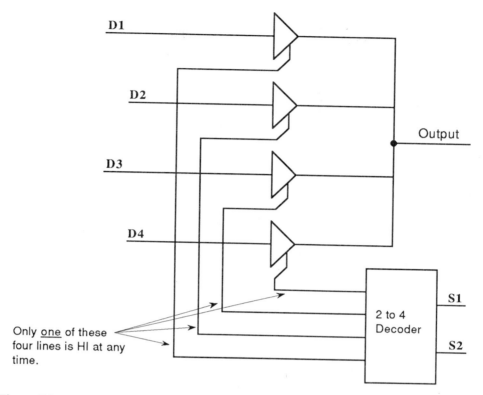

D1

D2

Output

D3

D4

Only <u>one</u> of these
four lines is HI at any
time.

2 to 4
Decoder

S1

S2

Figure 9-9   A Simple Tri-state Buffer Circuit

9-10 shows a basic flip-flop and its truth table. Flip-flops are built with many configurations and special characteristics. Figure 9-11 shows several common flip-flop types and their truth tables.

You have no doubt noticed the appearance of a new input in the previous figure. A clock input is necessary when circuits require a timing pulse to operate. Because computers are high-speed devices, things must happen at precise times during their operation. A clock is responsible for the synchronization of all of the information within the computer. It en-sures that things happen at the right time with respect to each other.

Decoders and encoders are also important to logic circuits. A decoder is a device that has several inputs and outputs. A common decoder has two inputs and four outputs. One output line is made active for each of the four possible combinations of the inputs. Figure 9-12 shows a two-to-four decoder and its truth table. Decoders are often used to convert binary information to decimal form and to select output lines to enable functions based on input lines. You will see decoders used in the next section on circuits and applications.

Inputs		Clock Pulse	Outputs		Comments
S	R		Q	$\overline{Q}$	
0	0	↑	Q_0	$\overline{Q_0}$	No Change
0	1	↑	0	1	Reset
1	0	↑	1	0	Set
1	1	↑	X	X	Invalid

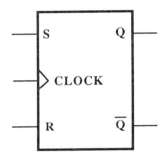

Figure 9-10   A Rising Edge-triggered S-R Flip-flop and Its Truth Table

An encoder's function is just the opposite of a decoder's. The encoder has more input lines than output lines. The binary number on the output lines is determined by the input line that is active. Figure 9-13 has the details.

The last two devices we will discuss here are the demultiplexer and the multiplexer. These are circuits that allow one input or output to be selected and the others to be put on hold. A demultiplexer has one data input, four data outputs, and two select inputs. The output line that is selected depends on the combination of the select bits. Figure 9-14 shows a demultiplexer and its truth table. Demultiplexers are used to send a signal to several different places, one place at a time. If you had four computer printers and you wanted to send output from your computer to any one of them, you could use a demultiplexer to select the printer that would receive each printout.

As you can guess, a multiplexer does the opposite of its counterpart. The multiplexer has four input lines and two select lines with only one output line. The select lines determine which of the inputs is sent to the output. Figure 9-15 demonstrates a typical multiplexer.

Now that you know something about these separate units, it's time to connect the circuits together and make them work.

Input	Clock Pulse	Outputs		Comments
D		Q	$\overline{Q}$	
0	↑	0	1	Reset
1	↑	1	0	Set

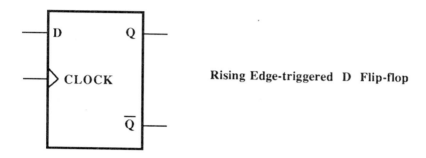

Rising Edge-triggered D Flip-flop

Inputs		Clock Pulse	Outputs		Comments
J	K		Q	$\overline{Q}$	
0	0	↑	Q_0	$\overline{Q_0}$	No Change
0	1	↑	0	1	Reset
1	0	↑	1	0	Set
1	1	↑	$\overline{Q_0}$	Q_0	Toggle

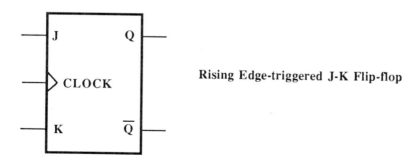

Rising Edge-triggered J-K Flip-flop

Figure 9-11   Common Flip-flops

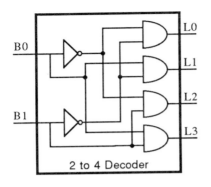

Inputs		Outputs			
B1	B0	L0	L1	L2	L3
0	0	1	0	0	0
0	1	0	1	0	0
1	0	0	0	1	0
1	1	0	0	0	1

Figure 9-12   A Decoder and Its Truth Table

CIRCUITS AND APPLICATIONS

Look at Figure 9-16. It has ten inputs and only one output. With the input of 1011001101, what is the output? Let's try to work through this logic circuit. When we get through, you will see that it only looks complicated and that it is easy to solve when broken down into simple circuits.

Start with the top three-input NAND gate. It has a 1,0,1 input. That would make the output inactive because all of the inputs are not active. With a bubble on the output, we know that its active state is low. Since we have an inactive output, as determined by the inputs, the gate puts a 1 out.

Now go to the two-input NOR gate, with inputs 4 and 5. With 4 high and 5 low, we know that the output will be active. From the output bubble, we know that the output will be low.

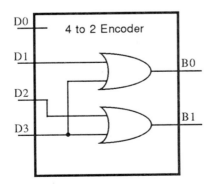

Inputs				Outputs	
D0	D1	D2	D3	B1	B0
1	0	0	0	0	0
0	1	0	0	0	1
0	0	1	0	1	0
0	0	0	1	1	1

Figure 9-13   An Encoder and Its Truth Table

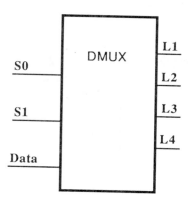

Inputs		Selected
S1	S0	Output Line
0	0	L1
0	1	L2
1	0	L3
1	1	L4

Figure 9-14   A Demultiplexer and Its Truth Table

Now we can go to the exclusive OR gate in the top middle. The top input from the NAND gate is 1 and the bottom input form the NOR gate is a 0. Since the inputs are different, the output of the exclusive will be active, or a 1 in this case (with no bubble). So we see that the top input to the final AND gate is a 1.

Now go to input 6. It runs into a tri-state inverter. The enable of the inverter is tied to input 7 and is a 1, so the inverter is enabled. The output of the inverter and thus the second input to the final AND gate is a 1.

Now look at input lines 7 and 8. They are both highs and go into an AND gate. The output of the AND gate will be active, in this case a low, because of the bubble on the output. So the first input to the bottom middle NAND gate is a 0.

Look at pins 9 and 10. They both go into an exclusive OR gate with some strange markings on the input. Pin 9 is a 0 and the active state of

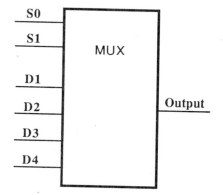

Input Line Control		Selected Input Data
S1	S0	Output
0	0	D1
0	1	D2
1	0	D3
1	1	D4

Figure 9-15   A Multiplexer and Its Truth Table

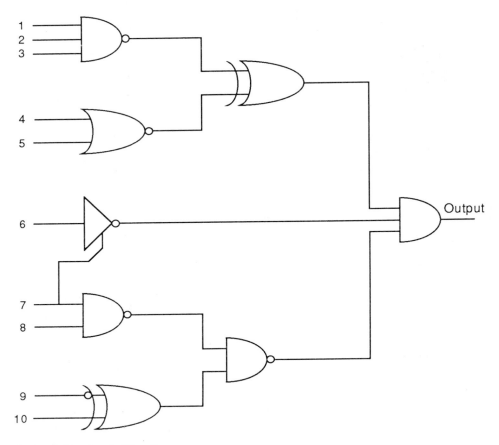

Figure 9-16   Logic Circuit

the input is low, as indicated by the bubble, so the top input is active. Pin 10 is high and it is also active. With both inputs of an exclusive OR active, the output will be inactive, or a low in this case. This puts a 0 on the bottom input of the NAND gate.

Remembering that we had a 0 on the top input, we now know that both inputs are low, which makes the output of the gate inactive, or a 1, which is the final input to the final AND gate.

With all ones, the final AND gate will have an active output and put out a high. As you can see, it's not so complicated taken one step at a time.

Now go back and change each input one at a time and see if that affects the final output. Changing input 1 has no effect on the output; however, changing pin 2 to a high will change the output of the NAND gate to active and will change the final output. Continue through all of the input pins for more practice.

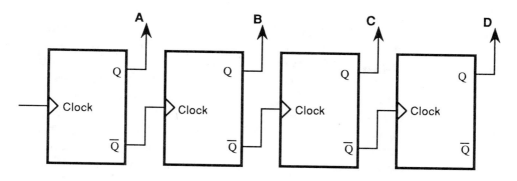

(Trigger on Leading Edge)

Pulse Count	Counter Output			
	D	C	B	A
1	0	0	0	1
2	0	0	1	0
3	0	0	1	1
4	0	1	0	0
5	0	1	0	1
6	0	1	1	0
7	0	1	1	1
8	1	0	0	0
9	1	0	0	1
10	1	0	1	0
11	1	0	1	1
12	1	1	0	0
13	1	1	0	1
14	1	1	1	0
15	1	1	1	1
16	0	0	0	0

Figure 9-17   4-bit Binary Counter

Now let's look at an application for flip-flops. We will build a 4-bit, binary output pulse counter. Look at Figure 9-17 and follow through the pulses.

The flip-flops used here are the T, or toggle, type that change states on the upward transition of each pulse. When the first pulse arrives, the output of the first flip-flop goes high and the counter output becomes 0001. When the second pulse arrives, the output of the first flip-flop toggles and the second flip-flop changes states. This changes the counter output to 0010. The third pulse comes in and changes the first flip-flop again but the second does not change, so the counter output is now 0011. The same procedure continues until the output of the counter is 1111, at which time the next count will be 0000. You can see that each counter divides the incoming signal by 2, the effect is that each flip-flop changes after it has received two pulses. Look at the chart of the outputs and the pulse counts and you will see that this circuit is a decimal-to-binary converter.

Now that you have a basic understanding of what digital logic is all about, you are ready to learn about computers.

CHAPTER REVIEW

On a separate sheet of paper, write a response to each question, statement, or problem below.

Short Answer

1. Find: a) the binary equivalent of decimal 38; b) the octal equivalent of decimal 38; and c) the hexadecimal equivalent of decimal 38.

2. Convert the following numbers to decimal: a) binary 110011; b) octal 170; and c) hexadecimal A0.

3. Explain the basic difference between an encoder and a decoder.

4. Describe the difference between a multiplexer and a demultiplexer.

5. What is the function of a buffer? How is it used?

10

An Introduction to Computers

Today, computers come in all shapes and sizes; no other field is undergoing such rapid change. Because computers affect our lives in so many ways, it is important that we understand how they work.

BASIC CONFIGURATIONS

Computing machines can be divided into two broad categories, analog and digital, based on their primary method of operation. Today, when one thinks of a computer, it is a digital machine that comes to mind. Digital computers process information by the use of digital electronics, which we learned a little about in the previous chapter. These machines work with two voltage levels, using the binary number system to process information. Analog computers, on the other hand, simulate actual problem situations by using electronic components and varying voltages and currents to approximate those situations. For example, suppose the designers of an oil refinery wanted to be able to predict the level of oil in a temporary storage tank that would have four input lines, all at variable pumping volumes, and three output lines, also pumping at different rates. A simulation could be set up on an analog computer by building a circuit in which the maximum circuit voltage is used to represent the storage capacity of the tank. The input lines would represent the incoming oil and the individual currents would be proportional to the respective flow rates. The same could be done for the outputs. The voltage across the circuit then indicates the level of oil in the tank. This is a simple example, but it serves to illustrate how analog computers are used.

For the rest of this book, when we say computer, we mean a digital computer. Digital machines are much more popular than their analog counterparts and outnumber them in usage. As you may remember from

Chapter 1, the first digital computer was constructed in 1946, but computing machines did not become practical until transistors became available.
The first computers were very large, filling many rooms with their data
processing equipment. The size breakthrough came with the invention of
the integrated circuit.

Integrated circuits, or ICs, as they are called, allow many circuits to
be placed on a single silicon "chip," which is about the diameter of a
pencil eraser and thinner than a dime (and contains thousands of the gates
and devices discussed in the previous chapter). This chip is put in a sealed
plastic package with only the connecting wires extending outside the
package. The most common package is the dual-in-line package, or DIP.
DIPs are commonly found in 4- to 40-pin configurations. All kinds of
circuits are placed in them and most computer circuits are contained in
IC-DIPs.

Many standard ICs can be bought at electronics supply stores. There
is also an entire industry devoted to the design and manufacture of custom chips. Custom chips are often desirable when many copies of the
same product are going to be produced; a custom chip can be designed to
take the place of several chips in the product. Custom chips that are designed specifically for one function are called ASICs, for application-
specific integrated circuits. ASICs are becoming more popular as the costs
of design and production decrease and the value of the chips becomes
more important to the company producing the device with the ASIC in it.

Figure 10-1   Typical Dual-in-line Package (DIP) (Courtesy of National Semiconductors
Corp., Santa Clara, CA)

After a design engineer decides which ICs should be used, or designs new chips, the task is to properly connect them all together. This is commonly done by using a printed circuit (PC) or printed wiring board. The PC board is a thin (1/16 to 1/8 inch, or 1.7 to 3.2 mm thick) piece of fiber board or ceramic that has all of the interconnections (conductive paths) between the chips fixed to the board itself. These electrical connections are in the form of copper and solder tracks that look like little roadways all over the surface of the board. This eliminates the need for all the wires that would be required to interconnect the components of the circuit.

The chips are simply placed with the pins extending through the holes in the board and then soldered into position. The solder makes the electrical contact and also holds the chip in place. If we are making a single-board system, when all of the integrated circuits are on the board, the computer is finished. It must then be connected with the necessary support components that provide power and allow communication with the outside world, and put into a cabinet. One edge of any circuit board

Figure 10-2   Typical Printed Circuit Board

usually has a row of pins which plug into a socket. This connects the computer to the necessary switches, lights, indicators, and other equipment. The entire computer is also mounted in a case which serves as a frame to hold the components and as a shield to protect the circuits from electrical interference or physical damage.

Now that we know a little about computer hardware, we can move on to how a computer system works. Figure 10-3 shows a simplified diagram of the internal structure of a computer system. As you can see, the diagram is grouped into major sections or blocks. These are the processor, sometimes called the CPU (central processing unit); the calculating device (or math coprocessor), sometimes called the ALU (for arithmetic logic unit); the memory; mass storage; and the input and output devices, called I/O (for input/output). In the next sections we will discuss these in detail.

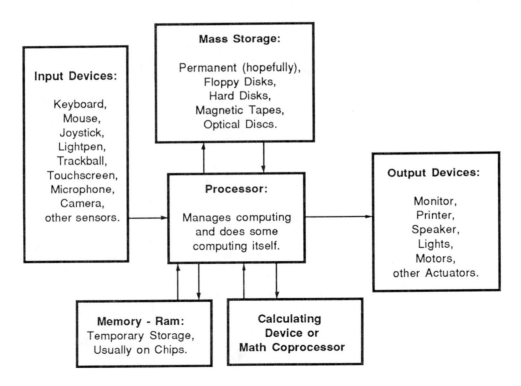

Figure 10-3   Computer System Block Diagram

THE CENTRAL PROCESSING UNIT

The central processing unit, or CPU, is the most important part of the computer. It is, in fact, the "brain" or supervisor of the system. As shown in Figure 10-3, the CPU is at the center of the system, like a supervisor in a company. The supervisor directs activity and makes sure that work gets done in an orderly fashion. A CPU fulfills the same function in a computer system.

Besides managing instructions and information in the system, the CPU also controls all of the input and output to and from the computer. Input to the computer usually takes one of two forms, data or programs. Data is simply information; it could be a file with the names, addresses, and phone numbers of your friends, or all the names of the albums in your record collection. Programs, however, are a special kind of data which give the computer precise, step-by-step instructions for the tasks it is to accomplish. For example, a program might ask the computer to list your record albums in alphabetical order. Without instructions on how to perform the task, the computer would not know what to do and would be completely useless.

Both data and programs go to the central processing unit. They usually enter either through one of the input devices or through one of the mass storage devices, typically a floppy disk. The CPU directs the data to either the memory or the I/O, depending on the program. When it receives a program instruction, it decodes it and then directs the other sections of the computer in the manner necessary to execute the instruction.

THE ARITHMETIC LOGIC UNIT

The ALU works very closely with the CPU. In Figure 10-3, it is located in the lower right portion of the diagram. The ALU is responsible for all of the calculations that the computer performs. All of the common arithmetic functions — addition, subtraction, multiplication, division, and trigonometric relationships — are built into the ALU. When the CPU receives an instruction that requires a calculation, it simply instructs the ALU to perform the necessary math and return the answer to it. Today the ALU and the CPU are usually combined into one IC chip. This is to conserve space and to speed up the operation of the computer. These integrated ALU and CPU chips are referred to as microprocessors and are the heart of the modern personal computer.

Special variations of ALUs, known as math coprocessors, are also available for many small computers. Math coprocessors are separate IC chips that do only mathematical calculations. These chips are able to handle complex calculations more quickly than the ALU in the microprocessor chip. The result is a faster computer system because the coprocessor chip shares the work load with the microprocessor.

THE MEMORY

The memory is the part of the computer that stores the programs and data for the microprocessor. In the block diagram of Figure 10-3, the memory is shown in the lower left. The memory is made up of many chips that provide many bits of storage. Each bit in memory has a specific location or address. In order for the CPU to store something in memory, it must first know the address at which it wishes to store the information. When it has found the address, the CPU then puts the information in the memory location where it belongs.

Several types of memory are found in a computer system. These are: RAM (random access memory), ROM (read only memory), EPROM (erasable programmable read only memory), and EEPROM (electrical erasable programmable read only memory). You may wonder what the difference is between these types of memory. RAM is memory that allows you to put information in and take it out again. This is known as writing (putting information in) and reading (taking information out of) the memory. RAM is the easiest kind of memory to use, but it has one major drawback. It is volatile; that is, it must have constant electrical power to preserve what is stored in it. All of the other types of memory listed above do not have this restriction. ROM is used for information or programs in the system that do not change, and is independent of electrical power. When ROM is created, the program and data are placed in it. This information may only be read; it cannot be changed or lost. EPROM and EEPROM are special kinds of ROM that may be programmed more than once, but only with special equipment. Both of these memory types are also permanent, unless they are reprogrammed.

INPUT/OUTPUT (I/O) PORTS AND DEVICES

The circuits that handle the data flow to and from the outside world are called I/O, or input/output circuits (see Figures 10-4 and 10-5). These enable the computer to interact with other devices and people. The I/O

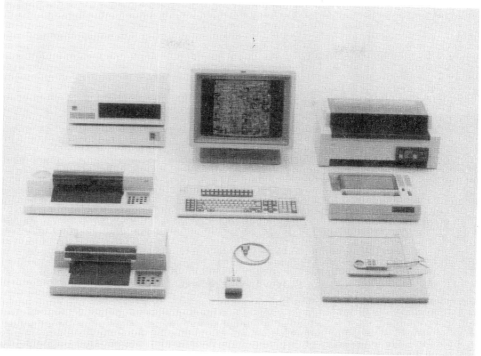

Figure 10-4 Typical Input Devices: Keyboard; Light Pen; Joysticks; Mouse (Courtesy of International Business Machines Corp.)

sections can be seen in Figure 10-3 at the upper left and at the right. The input devices are the means by which information enters the computer. The output devices allow the computer to communicate with us, and enables other things to work.

Input/output device operations are generally the slowest of the computer. The other blocks of the computer, such as the microprocessor and the memory, run much faster than the I/O. In most cases, design engineers must build the system so the CPU can slow down enough for the I/O. It is the I/O speed that we notice when we interact with the computer. The computer that seems to operate the most efficiently will be the one with the quickest I/O.

MASS STORAGE

This is the block shown at the top of Figure 10-3. You probably know mass storage as floppy and hard disks. These are the devices that get data in

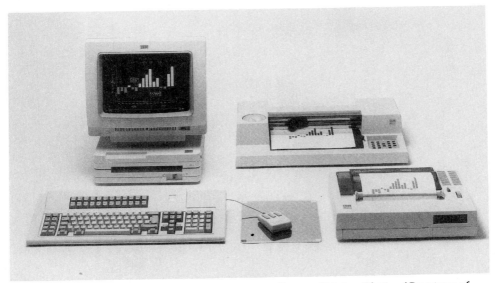

Figure 10-5   Common Types of Output Devices: Screen; Printer; Plotter (Courtesy of International Business Machines Corp.)

and out of the computer at high speeds. Without mass storage capability, we would spend hours typing in simple programs to run the computer and entering even small amounts of data would become a major task. Most disk drives today use magnetic methods to record and read data, but newer devices that use light for the same functions are being developed.

CHAPTER REVIEW

On a separate sheet of paper, write a response to each question, statement, or problem below.

Short Answer

1. Describe the difference between analog and digital computers.
2. What is the purpose of printed circuit boards? Where are they used?
3. What is a CPU? Why is it considered the most important part of a computer?
4. In what way does an ALU differ from a CPU?

5. List the different types of memory.
6. Describe the main differences between ROM and RAM.
7. What is an EPROM?
8. Compared to a ROM, what advantages might an EPROM have?
9. List the different input and output devices.

True or False

1. Printed circuit boards are composed of many ICs.
2. The CPU controls all of a computer's input and output.
3. To process the arithmetic calculations, the ALU sends data to the CPU.
4. The program and data are stored in a computer's memory.
5. Information in the ROM can only be read; it cannot be changed.
6. When electrical power to the RAM is turned off, the information in the RAM is lost.
7. A mouse and a joystick are input devices.

11

Putting Computers to Work

INTRODUCTION

Now that you know a little about the components and construction of computers, you are ready to look at how they are used. In this chapter, you will learn some of the basics of computer numbering systems, languages, operations, hardware, and software.

PROGRAMMING AND LANGUAGES

As you learned in the previous chapter, in order for a computer to be useful it must first be programmed. Programming is the term used to describe the process of giving the computer a series of orders to accomplish a task. Programs instruct the computer on the moving, storing, and manipulation of data. There are many different ways to program a computer and these ways have changed greatly since the computer was invented.

Early computer programming was done in machine code, which is the series of binary 1's and 0's covered in Chapter 9. Machine code gets its name from the fact that it is directly understandable by the computer. To write a program using this code, the user first had to determine the steps, or orders, he or she wanted the computer to accomplish. Afterwards, a programmer would work with a series of charts to translate the program into machine code manually. For example, an instruction that directed the computer to output some value could look like this: OUT 03. This instruction directs the computer to send some information to a certain port (the name for funnels and chutes). In this case the port is numbered 03. This seems straightforward enough, but, in fact, the computer cannot understand this instruction at all. It must first be translated into machine code. The machine code for this instruction might look like this: $110100110011_{(2)}$.

Since programs are responsible for everything a computer does, they can become quite lengthy and complex. In the early days of computers, every computer function — word processing, spell checking, calculations, graphics — was the result of a program that had been written and then translated into machine code. As you may imagine, though, translating a long program into machine code is a very tedious and error-prone process. It soon became clear that another way had to be devised to make the user's desires known and understandable to the computer.

The outcome of this desire to make programming easier was the creation of programming languages. A programming language is a way of instructing the computer with an English-like syntax. The code written is then run through a program called a compiler that automatically translates the English-like words into a machine code that the computer can understand. Today there are numerous programming languages, too many to even mention here. However, some languages are widely used and play a very important part in programming today's computers.

The first language is called assembler. It is the closest language-to-machine code. Through a series of one-, two-, or three-word commands, the user instructs the computer to perform the desired operations. Assembler shares some of the disadvantages of machine code. It can be very hard to use because it is quite far removed from common language. The advantage of writing in assembler is speed. Programs created and compiled with an assembler run much faster on a computer than any other language, except machine code itself. Because of its close relationship to machine code, assembler is sometimes referred to as a low-level language.

Most other computer languages are considered to be high-level languages; that is, they are more closely related to our written language, making them easier to use. Most high-level languages are usually designed around a particular need and are therefore more useful for certain applications than others. FORTRAN, short for FORmula TRANslation, is a language designed for mathematical and scientific calculations. This is not to say that it cannot do anything else. It just means that this language is primarily for mathematics. Other languages that are in wide use today include BASIC (an easy-to-learn language for teaching programming), COBOL (a business language), Pascal (another teaching language), and C language (mostly for systems programming). The thing that all of these languages have in common is the trade-off between English-like programming and speed. Programs written in any of these languages will run slower than the same program in assembler or machine code. Sometimes this difference in efficiency is critical and the programs must be written in a low-level language, but if speed is not a consideration, a higher-level language can certainly be used.

Adding Two Numbers

Step	Address	Bytes	Instruction	Comments
1	0500*	2**	LDA #05	Puts 05 in Accumulator
2	0502	3	STA 0C0A	Stores 05 at 0C0A
3	0505	2	LDA #09	Puts 09 in Accumulator
4	0507	3	ADC 0C0A	Adds 05 and 09
5	050A	3	STA 0C0B	Stores 0E in 0C0B
6	050D	1	BRK	Stop

*   The starting address selected for this program.

** The number of bytes of memory taken up by the instruction. Notice that the addresses where each instruction is stored increase to allow for the full instruction to be stored.

Included in the table above are instructions for a program that adds two numbers and stores the result in a specified memory location.

Steps 1 through 3 store the first number and get the second number into the accumulator. Step 4 recalls the first number from memory and adds it to the second number. The fifth step stores the sum in memory location 0C0B. Step 6 stops the program.

This example illustrates that machine language programs require many steps, even to do very simple tasks.

Figure 11-1   Sample Assembler Code Program

HARDWARE VS. SOFTWARE

Hardware and software are two essential parts of the computer system. Hardware refers to the physical components of the computer system: the IC chips, the microprocessor, the monitor screen, etc. This is the part of the system that is constant and can be used for numerous applications without requiring modification. Software, on the other hand, refers to the programs that instruct the hardware to do things in order to accomplish a task. While the average user is not involved in the creation of a computer system's hardware, he or she can, and frequently does, create software. Software is the medium that is transferable between computers. What is created on one computer can be taken to another computer of the same type and it will work there also. The main distinction between the two is that software is what gives orders to the hardware.

Recently, though, the difference between hardware and software has become much smaller. This is due to the introduction of something called firmware. Firmware is sort of a hybrid of hardware and software. It plays a major part in most of today's personal computers. Firmware is software contained in a hardware package that is built into the design of the computer system. For example, firmware can be a program that is put into a ROM or EPROM chip and then built into the design of the computer system. This program can be the operating system used to access different parts of the computer hardware, such as printers, keyboards, or displays. As you can see, this is a middle ground of sorts. Even though the firmware is a program (like software), it is also a permanent and fixed part of the system (like hardware). Firmware packages have become very common because they reduce the amount of hardware and software necessary in a system and because they are relatively inexpensive to reproduce in the large quantities needed for full-scale production of computer systems.

BATCH VS. INTERACTIVE

There are two kinds of interaction with a computer system; these are the batch mode and the interactive mode. The kind used depends on the needs of the user.

Batch mode computer operations run all at one time, usually without the need for a keyboard and monitor or other user intervention. The user creates a file that contains the commands and data the computer needs to run the program. This file is then sent to the computer to be executed at a predetermined time when the system resources are available, perhaps an hour or even days later. Then the computer system reads the batch file and executes each command in it, one after the other. A printed copy indicating the responses made by the computer in answer to the commands in the batch file is also usually made. This is so the programmer can trace and correct any errors that surface during the execution of the batch file. The batch mode method of interaction has advantages and disadvantages. If there are errors in the batch file, the whole process must be started over again, possibly taking another hour or day. On the other hand, the user is not required to sit and watch over a set of commands that may take a long time to execute. Today, batch mode operation is used considerably less than in the past, but it is still favored for a variety of specific functions.

The other common method of computer use is the interactive mode. In this mode of operation the user gives the commands to the computer through a keyboard and monitor, one at a time. Every command that the user inputs to the computer is executed immediately. The results are displayed on the user's monitor screen. This mode is quicker for short or error-prone jobs that require much attention and guidance from the operator of the system.

Due to the ever-increasing power and speed of computers, the interactive mode is becoming more common than the batch mode of operation; nevertheless, there are still times when the batch mode is practical and preferred. In most cases the computer system supports both modes of operation, leaving the choice of which one to use up to the operator.

REAL-WORLD INTERACTION

In order for the computer to do any useful work, it must be able to communicate not only with us, but also with other devices in the real world. The devices that allow us to communicate with the computer and connect it to other machines are called input/output or I/O devices. (These devices were introduced in the previous chapter.)

The normal way that a person communicates with a computer is by means of a keyboard (which looks like a typewriter) and a monitor. These two devices may be combined in one unit and referred to as a terminal. As you press each key on the keyboard, its corresponding letter is sent electronically to the computer. At the same time, the letter is displayed on your monitor so that you may correct what you have typed if you made a mistake. The monitor is also used by the computer to show its responses to your commands.

But what about other kinds of machines? How do they work with computers? As you may recall from earlier chapters, computers use the binary number system for internal operations. The real world does not work on the two-state; it requires a full range of values and meanings, known as analog values. For example, the sound intensity of a stereo system may be adjusted to a range of levels instead of just sound on or sound off. In order for the computer to communicate with the world outside, there must be some way to translate the analog values of the real world to the binary values of the computer world. Conversely, there must also be a way for the binary computer to control external analog machines.

Analog-to-digital and digital-to-analog converters are the means by which computers communicate with processes of the outside world. An analog-to-digital converter is an input device that takes a value of something from the real world and translates it into its binary equivalent. A digital-to-analog converter is simply the opposite of an analog-to-digital one, with a binary number being translated to its analog equivalent and sent out of the computer.

Other kinds of common input and output devices are based on these principles. Consider the joystick in Figure 11-2. The joystick is an analog device. It translates the direction and distance that the handle has been moved into two voltages which can take on different values, depending on the amount of movement made. These voltages are sent to an analog-to-digital converter, which translates them into binary numbers equal to the values of the voltages that it read. These numbers then cause a corresponding change on the display. The same process is involved in an output device, such as a small robot arm. The robot arm is an analog device that can be moved in different directions and at different speeds by outputting various voltages to it. The computer controls this device by sending binary numbers that represent the analog voltages to a digital-to-analog converter, which changes them to real voltage

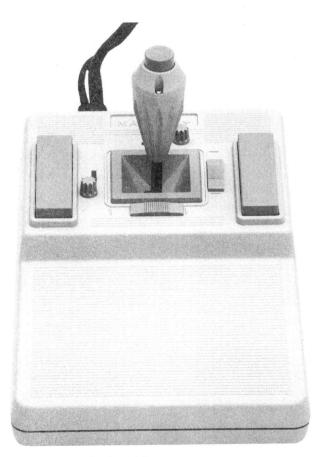

Figure 11-2   The Joystick

values that direct the robot. The possibilities of I/O are limited only by the kinds of devices we can find that will send information to the computer and the devices we can control by computer.

SIZES AND USES

Computers are used in varying degrees in different places in the world. To accommodate the different needs for computing power, various sizes of computers are manufactured. The basic sizes are, from largest to smallest, the mainframe computer, the minicomputer, and the microcomputer.

Mainframes are the large computers found most often in universities, large research labs, big business corporations, and government centers. They are used where a relatively large number of people must simultaneously have access to a lot of computing power and storage. These computers serve many people through time-sharing. This means that the computer accesses each and every person using it and takes commands solely from that person for a certain segment of time. After that segment of time is over, the computer accesses the next person and repeats the process. The switching between users is done so quickly that it seems, to the individual user, that he or she is the only one using the computer. Besides allowing time-sharing, a mainframe can store and manipulate large amounts of information, usually a gigabyte or more, at high speed. A gigabyte of information is a billion letters, or characters of data. When a very large amount of information must be stored or manipulated, a mainframe usually does the job.

The middle category is occupied by the computers that are classified as minicomputers. These computers can also be time-sharing, or they can be single-user systems, which means only one person may use the computer's resources at one time. Minicomputers are used in smaller companies, universities, and in industry. These computers are often used for business purposes such as preparing company reports or controlling factory operations. The storage capacity for these computers is usually several hundred megabytes, or one million characters of data. The minicomputer may soon cease to exist, due to the rapid advances in speed and capability of its little brother, discussed in the next section.

The microcomputer is the type of computer that you have most likely had contact with already. The popular and ever-present desktop computer is an example of the microcomputer. Other uses of a microcomputer include industrial and robotic control, statistical analysis, and programming. The difference between the microcomputer and the minicomputer is becoming very vague. Microcomputers now have the capacity to store a few hundred megabytes of data. It has been suggested that the minicomputer is really the most advanced form of the microcomputer or that the microcomputer is the lowest form of the mini. Whatever the case, the gap between these two classifications is sure to become smaller in the future.

SUPERCOMPUTERS

There is actually a fourth size of computer: the supercomputer. Supercomputers are the big ones; they can perform millions of calculations per second. There are not too many of these machines and the military owns most of them. They are generally used for applications that require intense computer power, like satellite image enhancement, cryptographic code breaking, complex engineering analyses, and prediction of the weather. The company most well known for their supercomputers is Cray. Despite their vast computing power, Cray's supercomputers are not as big as you would expect. They are about the size of a chest-type freezer: large by today's computer standards but small compared to the mainframes of the 1950s.

As with most things in the computer field, we can expect the capabilities of supercomputers to increase also. New computing power could allow us to model the behavior of diseases and simulate treatments to aid medical research. We could determine that there is no winner in a global thermonuclear war. We could control all of the air traffic in the country with information obtained from navigation satellites. The list of possibilities is endless. These computers have the capability to allow us to analyze things we could never understand before because it took too much time to manipulate the data.

COMPUTER CRIMES AND VIRUSES

The issue of computer crimes is relatively new to society, but it is rapidly receiving more attention. We have heard in the news about people who sabotage computers and software to try to get back at someone for something. We know of "hackers," people who deliberately and with concentrated effort break into computers, networks, and data bases that they do not have legal access to. We have also heard of viruses — little sections of code that hide within programs or data and come out at predetermined times to cause mistakes in a computer. These are all examples of computer crime, a new field that our police and courts are not yet equipped to deal with.

Software today is very complex and seems to invite this type of behavior. There are people who know enough about computers to cause problems, and when one — or worse, a group — of these people decide to cause trouble, they sometimes succeed. Most of the efforts so far have focused on software. Proficient programmers who "go bad," try to introduce problems into the systems that they have access to. You probably heard of the programmer in Texas who was fired and subsequently got back into the computer and deleted much of the data base of the insurance company he had worked for. He was tried and convicted, but many computer criminals go undetected and unpunished.

There are literally thousands of computer viruses loose in the United States. I got a virus in my computer just recently when I got a disk from a friend who had been working on some drawings in a university computer lab. His disk had been infected and it, in turn, had infected my hard drive. I have since installed a virus detector program that checks every disk inserted into the computer. Some viruses are not too harmful; all they do is fill up your hard drive and slow down the computer; however, some viruses stay hidden for a while and then erase your data. If you are a computer user and share disks with others often, you should practice safe computing. Purchase and install a virus detector utility software package and upgrade it regularly. This will minimize your risk of becoming infected and hampering your computer system.

CHAPTER REVIEW

On a separate sheet of paper, write a response to each question, statement, or problem below.

Fill in the Blank

1. The closest language to machine code is _____.
2. Assembler is a _____ level language while FORTRAN is a _____ level language.
3. _____ level language is faster than _____ level language.
4. _____ is sort of a hybrid of hardware and software.
5. The two types of interaction with a computer system are the _____ mode and the _____ mode.

Short Answer

1. What is machine code?
2. What is the function of a compiler program?
3. Describe the difference between a high-level language and a low-level language.
4. Explain what computer software and hardware refer to.
5. What is the purpose of an analog-to-digital converter?
6. Describe the different types of computer, based on their size and uses.
7. Where is a mainframe typically used, and why?

12

Industrial Applications

INTRODUCTION

The manufacturing industries of the world are undergoing a major metamorphosis. Of course, electricity has played an essential part in manufacturing since the earliest assembly line factories, but what is happening today would boggle the mind of old Henry Ford. Automation is the wave of the future and we are in its whitewater now. Our factories are becoming push-button palaces and our workers are changing from machine operators into machine attendants. Gone are the days of the automotive assembly worker who installs ten nuts on the car as it passes by on the assembly line. Today's workers are smarter, more highly educated, more involved in the workplace, and have a greater stake in the operation. These are generalizations, of course, but if American industry is to survive the challenge of world competition, factory operations as we know them are destined for the history books.

ELECTRONIC CONTROLS

Except in the very early factories, electricity has been the energy source of choice for industrial operations. Electricity gave us the ability to operate very large machinery by pushing buttons and moving levers. Relays were used many years ago to control the operation of equipment and to make machines partially automatic. After the operator pushed the cycle start button, the first relay was energized; when the first part of the operation was completed, the movements of the machine closed the contacts on a switch and energized a second relay while de-energizing the first. When that operation was complete, another switch energized another relay, and so on. When the entire process was complete, the machine had completed one cycle; it then waited for the operator to tell it to start the whole process over again.

This type of relay automatic control was in widespread use until very recently and is still easy to find, but it is part of the technology of the past. Today, the standard device for machine control is the programmable logic controller, or PLC. PLCs are small computers (by today's standards) that are built with the power circuits to control all types of heavy equipment. They replace the relay panels of yesterday with one small cabinet filled with circuit boards and wires. Also, a new type of technician is required to maintain the newer machines. This is just a small example of the effect of advancing electronics on our lives.

PROCESS AUTOMATION

As computers first worked their way into our factories, digital electronics was used to control the position of motors and to provide position information to the operator. This type of early control was called numerical control, or NC. Numerical control machines have been around for the last fifteen years. They were generally run by a paper tape which contained the program or machine instructions. The program was usually created by an NC programmer. NC programmers were most often machinists who had taken an early interest in computer control of machining equipment. It was their job to lay out the tool paths needed to perform the required operations on the part and to transfer that information onto the tape for the machine to read.

When the machine was ready to run, the paper tape was loaded into the tape reader. The tape was then read by the machine and the machine went into action. All of the instructions needed to machine the workpiece were on the tape and the information was fed to the motors of the machine. In almost no time, the part was finished.

The machine operator was there to load and unload material, watch the machine to ensure that it didn't wreck itself, and monitor the quality of the operation. The productivity that was gained offset the costs incurred by adding another worker (the NC programmer) to the process.

The next step in the development of computer control was called CNC, or computer numerical control. In this step, the computer was tied directly to the machine tool and the programming was done at a computer terminal. When the programming was completed, the finished program was downloaded electronically to the machine for execution. The operator was still present to monitor the process for problems.

Today, as computers and other forms of digital control continue to invade the factory, the machines become more reliable, leaving the operators free to do other tasks.

PROCESS CONTROL AND FEEDBACK SYSTEMS

As advanced electronics works itself into factory operations, the processes become increasingly automated. The next necessary step in the development of fully automated systems was the implementation of process control systems. Process controls are built into the system to check the parts for errors or mistakes. At specific times during its operation, the machine interrupts the automated process and checks itself to determine if the parts meet specifications. If everything checks out, the operation proceeds normally; but if a problem is discovered, an alarm is sounded and the process is stopped. If the problem is minor or if the machine has the ability to correct the problem by adjusting the tooling or switching to another tool, the operation will continue. Figure 12-1 shows an example of a process control system.

Process control includes all parts of the operation that are used to check that things are proceeding properly. Many process controls are incorporated into what are called feedback loops. A feedback loop is created when a situation is monitored and is found to deviate from the expected; and a correction is made to return the situation to normal. An example might be helpful here. Figure 12-2 is an example of a simple feedback loop. The oven is a continuous cooking, moving-chain, pizza cooker, similar to many in use today. The operator sets the control of the chain speed controller to the time that the pizza should stay in the oven. A signal is sent to the motor that drives the chain to tell the motor how fast to turn.

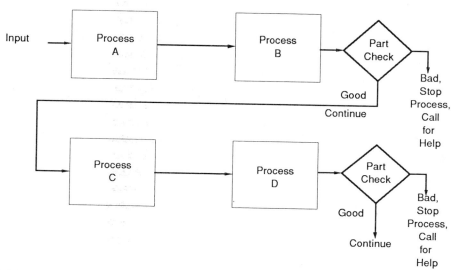

Figure 12-1   A Process Control System

Inside the motor, there are sensors that send a signal out of the motor and back to the controller that tells exactly how fast the motor is actually turning. If there is any difference between how fast the motor is turning and how fast it should turn, the signal to the motor is corrected. This is called a closed-loop feedback because the system is capable of correcting itself to operate at the proper speed. If the pizzas are getting overcooked, the operator simply turns the speed control so that the motor runs a little faster and the pizza spends less time in the oven.

In contrast, an open-loop system is one in which the system cannot correct itself but must depend on operator action for any corrections. In an open-loop oven system, the control would only have a faster or slower knob for the speed adjustment. The pizza maker would have to determine how the pizzas were doing and make the proper adjustments. There is no provision in the system for it to sense its own operation and make adjustments.

Statistical process control, or SPC, is another type of process control. SPC used statistical analysis to determine if a process is functioning normally. Computers perform this analysis well; in many operations, they are hooked right into the machine to keep everything running smoothly.

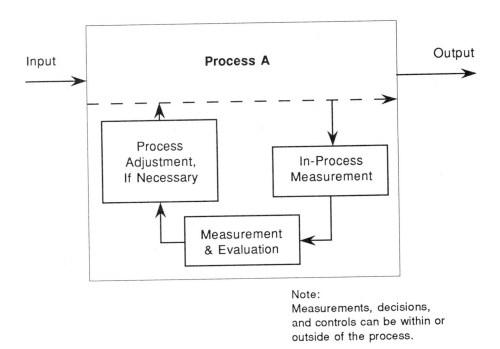

Note:
Measurements, decisions,
and controls can be within or
outside of the process.

Figure 12-2   A Closed-loop Feedback System

When the operation is underway, checks are taken on the parts and the measurements are sent to the computer. The computer then looks at this information in relation to many other readings and decides if the operation is progressing as it should. The computer can stop the operation if it determines that there is something wrong.

ROBOTICS

When robotics is mentioned, thoughts come to mind of human-like machines walking around our homes and factories. As they are currently implemented, however, robots usually look like only one part of a person, the arm. Factories use robots for many functions but most robots are built with a specific purpose or set of tasks in mind. The Robotics Institute of America (RIA) defines the robot as a programmable, multifunctional manipulator designed to move materials, parts, tools, or specialized devices through variable programmed motions for the performance of a variety of tasks. Robots are most commonly used for materials handling because they can lift and stack heavy boxes all day without getting tired. That is not to say that they don't break down, but robots make good materials handlers because lifting and stacking requires no thinking, just tireless performance. Figure 12-3 shows a materials handling robot.

Figure 12-3   A Materials Handling Robot .

Figure 12-4   A Component Insertion Robot

As robots become equipped with more advanced features, such as improved tactile sensing and machine vision, they are used for a wider variety of tasks. Many robots are now used for electronic product assembly. Robots are very good for mounting the components on a printed circuit board. Newer robots with fine control and high accuracy of movement can be used for delicate assembly work. Figure 12-4 shows a robot selecting components (metal wheels) for insertion in an automatic "creeper."

After robots were introduced and became practical to use in the workplace, many people predicted that they would take over our manufacturing operations. This has not come true for several reasons. First, robots are expensive to purchase and to operate. They require preventive and corrective maintenance, and their operation must be monitored. If an unskilled person is replaced by an unskilled robot, often the total operation costs do not decrease and occasionally they will increase. Robots should be used only in situations where they offer a distinct advantage over the use of a person in the same job. Many manufacturers implemented robots early on to avoid being left behind, only to find that the productivity increase did not offset the increase in costs. Those companies that are moving ahead successfully with the use of robots are careful in selecting the applications for robot implementation that work most efficiently.

Now that you know something about robotics applications, you are ready to learn about the robots themselves. A robot consists of four basic systems: the mechanical or physical system, the power or drive system, the end tooling or hand, and the control unit. The following paragraphs will describe these systems.

The mechanical system is the structure of the robot. The arm, the base, and all of the other mechanical parts make up this system. Generally speaking, a robot's construction determines what it can be used for. The mechanical system is designed to give the robot a certain number of degrees of freedom and a particular work envelope. These two terms describe roughly what a robot can do and how far it can reach. A degree of freedom for a robot means that the robot is capable of movement in a certain plane or direction. If the base of a robot can rotate, it has one degree of freedom. If the robot can also raise and lower its arm, it has two degrees of freedom. If it can move its arm in and out (extend and retract), it has three degrees of freedom. If it can move its wrist up and down, it has four degrees of freedom. Add wrist rotation, and five degrees are available. As you can see, the more degrees of freedom a robot has, the more flexible it is for various applications. Figures 12-5a, b, c, and d show several types of robots and list their degrees of freedom and their parts.

The power system for the robot is its muscles. Three types of power systems are in general use. They are electrical, hydraulic, and pneumatic. As you can guess, an electrical system uses electric motors to make the robot move. Electrical systems are used for robots that need precise and highly controlled movements, but not for ones that must lift heavy loads. When brute force is needed, hydraulic systems are used. A hydraulic pump is the power source for this system, with the necessary control valves operated by the control system. In a pneumatic system, compressed air supplies the power to move the robot. Figure 12-6 shows a chart of the pros and cons of each type of power system and the types of robots it is used for.

The end tooling of every robot is different. End tooling is sometimes called end-of-arm tooling, the end effector, or the robot's hand. All of these terms refer to the same thing: the point at which the robot grasps the part or workpiece it is handling. The end tooling differs depending on the purpose of the robot. Obviously, the hand that is used to move a brick would not be used to move an egg. In many cases, the end tooling is designed after the application for the robot has been decided. In specialized applications like spray painting, the end tooling is a spray gun. For

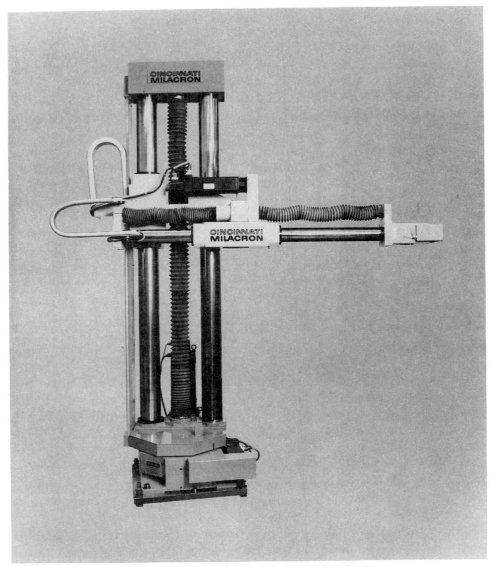

Figure 12-5a   Typical Industrial Robots (Courtesy of Cincinnati Milacron Inc.)

welding, a welding head is attached to the end of the robot arm. Figure 12-7 shows some common end-of-arm tooling.

The part of the robot most appropriate for this book is the control system. This system is usually a computer of some type. One of the attributes of most robots is that they are easily reprogrammable; that is, their

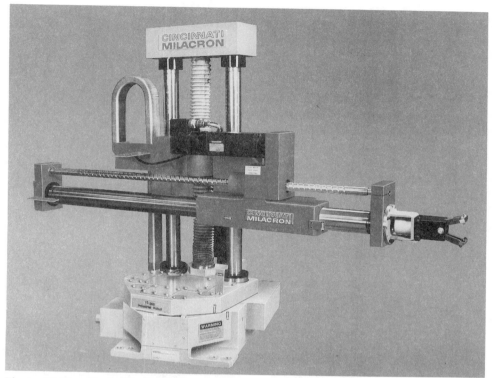

Figure 12-5b   Typical Industrial Robots (Courtesy of Cincinnati Milacron Inc.)

routine can be easily changed by modifying the control program. The program is the input to the control system. It is the instruction set for the robot and describes, in computer language, the duties the robot is to perform. The computer accepts this program and then tells each of the robot motors when to run, how fast to run, and when to stop. Sophisticated control systems are responsible for the utility of today's robots.

Some control systems use their own language. Unimate, a major robot manufacturer of industrial robots, has its own language, named VAL. IBM also has a language for its robots. These languages have been developed to answer the need for better ways to translate into computer commands the position and movement information for activating the robot. Generally speaking, if you can program a computer in any simple language, you can learn to program a robot. Some robots use the walk-through, or teach, method of programming. To program this type of robot requires no computer skill or training. To create a program, the robot control unit is set at the learn, or teach, mode. Then the robot is manually

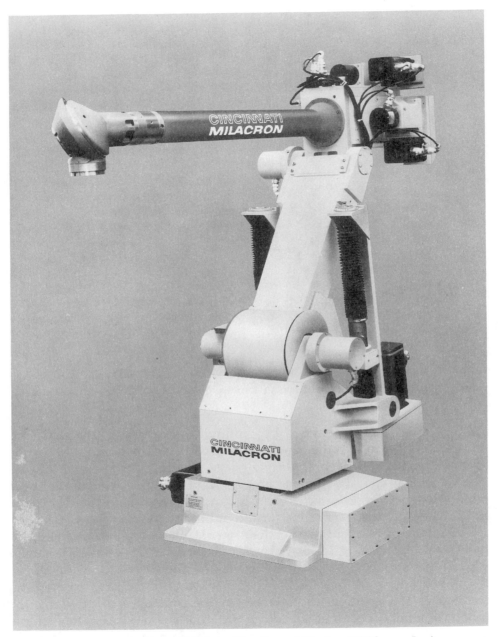

Figure 12-5c   Typical Industrial Robots (Courtesy of Cincinnati Milacron Inc.)

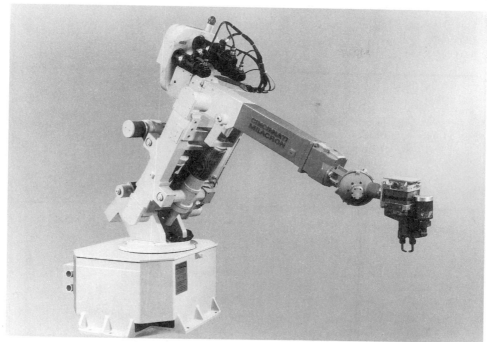

Figure 12-5d   Typical Industrial Robots (Courtesy of Cincinnati Milacron Inc.)

moved through the series of movements that will be its programmed operation. During this time, the control unit memorizes the movements of the robot. When one cycle of the operation is complete, the learn mode is stopped and the sequence can be repeated once or any number of times under the instruction of the control unit. Figure 12-8 shows a robot teach pendant, the device used for teaching the robot its job.

Although robots are very useful machines, their use in the U.S. workplace has not been as widespread as was predicted. Many manufacturers are using more process automation and fewer robots because of cost and productivity trade-offs. The next section discusses the direction of our manufacturing industries.

AUTOMATED WORK CELLS

An automated work cell is the name given to a collection of machines that run automatically, loading and unloading their own parts, checking these parts for defects, and requiring only spot-checking and bulk materials

POWER SOURCE	STRENGTHS	DRAWBACKS	TYPES OF ROBOTS
Electrical	• Readily Available • Widely Distributed • Excellent System Precision • Fine Motion Control	• Electrical Safety Must Be Observed • Can Not Use In Explosive Environment	• Insertion • Assembly • Some Pick And Place, Material Handling • Usually Small Robots With High Accuracy Requirements
Hydraulic	• Large Payload Capacity • Good Combination Of Speed, Lifting Capacity, And Precision	• Installation And Maintenance Are Expensive • Requires Considerable Maintenance • Some Hydraulic Fluids Are Flammable	• Material Handling • Large Systems
Pneumatic	• Inexpensive • Can Hook Up To Central Air System Or Run From Local Compressor • High Speed Operation	• Mechanical Programming Necessary For Stops • Poor Application For Systems Requiring Precise Motion Control	• Pick And Place • Material Handling • Used In Expensive Environments

Figure 12-6   Power System Characteristics

handling from workers. These work cells may or may not have robots in them. They are usually composed of several pieces of machining equipment, materials handling equipment, automatic inspection equipment, and the work cell control unit that tells all of the pieces what to do and when to do it. Figure 12-9 is a block diagram of a typical work cell.

Some long assembly lines are designed all at one time, but, in many cases, the operations in the manufacture of a product are automated one at a time by creating individual work cells. When all of the cells are operating, they can be connected to each other with the required materials

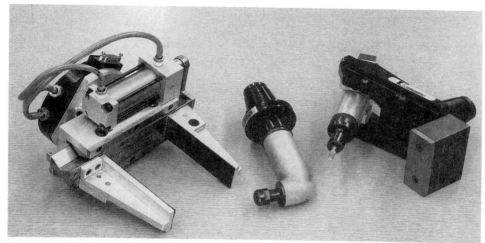

Figure 12-7 End Effectors

Figure 12-8 A Robot Teach Pendant

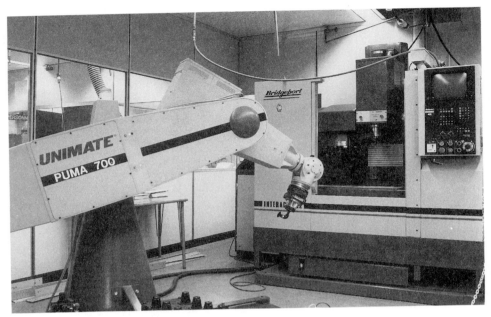

Figure 12-9   A Part-machining Work Cell

handling equipment, creating an entirely automated system. Unless a company has lots of money to invest in process automation to automate entire operations at once, individual work cell automation is preferable. Work cell control units can be tied into a central computer to receive their instructions but usually are programmed on the shop floor. When all of the operations in manufacturing are tied into a central computer, a new field is entered — computer-integrated manufacturing.

COMPUTER-INTEGRATED MANUFACTURING

CIM, as computer-integrated manufacturing is called, is the culmination of computer-controlled manufacturing. CIM links all of the production operations together through distributed control and a central data base that contains all information about all parts and operations necessary for the running of the plant. Figure 12-10 shows a typical CIM control room.

As we discussed earlier, factory automation started with NC equipment operating from computer instructions. The operations were

Figure 12-10 CIM Control Room (Courtesy of Allen-Bradley)

computer controlled but there was no interconnection of them. When CNC came along, the operations were linked through a common computer but everything still ran separately. The next step was the creation of work cells on the shop floor and finally the total automation of the production lines. Figure 12-11 is a picture of Allen-Bradley's completely automated product line at their contacts plant in Milwaukee, Wisconsin. Figure 12-12 shows a close-up of an automated assembly line from this plant.

While all of this was happening on the shop floor, the product design and drafting processes were also getting computerized. Historically, the field of design used the blueprint as its method of communication. To build a part, the design engineer visualized the part in his or her head and then, using traditional drafting as the communication language, created a blueprint. From this print, the personnel on the factory floor could

Figure 12-11   Automated Factory (Courtesy of Allen-Bradley)

manufacture the part. Whether the machinist took the print and manually produced the part or the CNC programmer created a tape to run the machine, the print was indispensable.

Within the last ten years, computer graphics has made great progress. There are now many computer systems, costing from $4,000 to $100,000, that allow the design engineer to sit at a computer terminal and create the drawings on the computer screen instead of on paper. This is called computer-aided design or computer-aided drafting, both abbreviated CAD. The CAD field has revolutionized the design and drafting jobs of today. We are no longer tied to the blueprints and, in fact, the parts are no longer drawn on blueprints. The master drawings are in a computer file containing all of the part information that was traditionally on the print. These files can now be passed between CAD systems so that when

Figure 12-12   Automated Assembly Line (Courtesy of Allen-Bradley)

a manufacturer wants to contract out a part, instead of mailing the blue-prints to the subcontractor, the computer file is transferred over the phone lines from one CAD system to the other.

The next obvious link was to hook these CAD files into the CNC equipment and have a direct link from the product design to the machines making the parts. This link is called computer-aided manufacturing, or CAM. CAM is the linking of computer files directly from the CAD system to the shop floor.

The step beyond CAM is CIM. CIM involves the linking of all the computers and automation control units into a fully computer-controlled and supervised process that can run a manufacturing facility. All CAD and CAM systems, automation control systems, accounting systems and information systems, handling of quality control data, shipping and

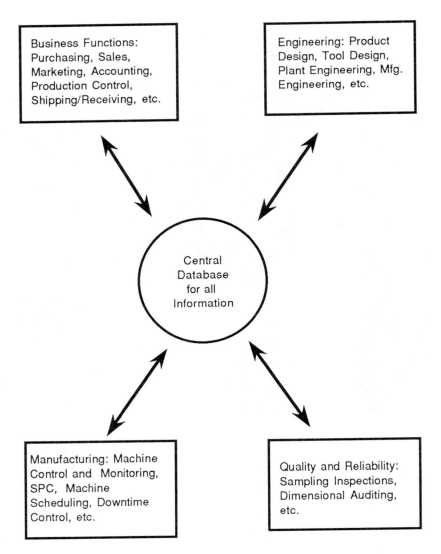

Figure 12-13   CIM in Operation

receiving information, maintenance scheduling for the equipment, and all other information about the entire operation is integrated to produce a single computer network. This network holds all the information needed to plan and execute the entire manufacturing operation. Figure 12-13 is a block diagram of a CIM system. This is the truly automated factory of the future.

CHAPTER REVIEW

On a separate sheet of paper, write a response to each question, statement, or problem below.

Short Answer

1. Explain the operation of a relay-type automatic machine.
2. What is the function of a PLC?
3. Compared to an NC machine, in what way is a CNC machine more advanced?
4. For process control, what is the difference between an open-loop system and a closed-loop system?
5. What is SPC and how does a computer assist in SPC?
6. List the four basic systems of a robot.
7. Describe what is meant by degrees of freedom.
8. List the types of power systems that are used for robots.
9. Explain the operation of an automated work cell.
10. Describe how a CIM process can be formed by integrating CAD and CAM systems.
11. Discuss applications for a CAD system or a CAM system.

13

Business Applications

INTRODUCTION

Today, business is one of the most complex and confusing of all the professions. Computers and electronics have played a dominant role in shaping the methods of current business operations. Business has always looked for, needed, and implemented tools to make its job of organizing the commerce of the day easier and more effective. Adding machines, based on mechanical principles, have been in use since the 1800s, although most businesses could not afford these early "computers." They were too costly and limited in use (only able to do the most simple mathematical operations). With the astounding advances in miniaturization, component manufacturing, and reliability, electronic calculators that could perform basic arithmetic operations became feasible and began to gain acceptance in the business world. At the same time, computers were improving rapidly in ability and usefulness. They became able to process, store, and display not only numeric data, but alphabetic (text) information as well. Today, a common business calculator can perform complex calculations, such as matrices and curve fitting (like electronic dot-to-dot, but using smooth, curved lines), with just the touch of a button. Computers have moved into the realm of a desktop accessory for most business people. Those who wish to succeed in today's market must become conversant with the operation and abilities of computers in order to make themselves competitively efficient and productive.

MANAGEMENT INFORMATION SYSTEMS

The management information system (MIS) is a popular topic in the business world today. There are many conflicting viewpoints about its definition alone. It has become a separate area of study in colleges and universities and there are now people who specialize in the design, implementation, and use of a management information system. What is a management information system, and why does it deserve so much study and controversy? We will attempt to define MIS by first breaking down the term into its component words and defining these in the context of the business world. The first word, management, can generally be defined as the directing of people toward the completion of a task. Information can be defined as the facts, figures, and data that are relevant to the business. Finally, a system can be defined as an interrelated group of elements. For our purposes, those elements would be the hardware and software of a computer system. Putting these words together in the context of business, an MIS is a collection of hardware and software for storing, manipulating, and displaying information that is relevant to managers and managing.

An MIS is intended to be a tool that managers can use, directly or through an MIS specialist, to help them coordinate the massive amounts of information that they require to make sound decisions in today's businesses. Other experts maintain, however, that MIS will go much further and, in fact, take over the job of managing in most of its known aspects. This argument is mostly a moot point. Management information systems will assume the burdens that the business world is willing to give to them, no more, no less. The pitfall to avoid is the notion that the MIS is infallible. These systems will only be as reliable as the hardware and software incorporated into their design. Within a limited range of applications, it may be possible that an MIS system can take over the decision-making process. However, the business world is so enormous that the design of an MIS cannot take into account all of the possibilities. Computers lack the creative capability to see the innovative changes in the business world; that is the realm of the business person. The computer may help a business person by providing more complex information, in better form, at a faster rate; but the last act, the intuition that brings the factors together into the decision, is performed by the human mind.

These systems, then, can provide numerous types of information for the manager. The information may be as simple as employee records, stored in the computer and available for recall by managers as needed, or as complex as the analysis of supply-and-demand factors on the current market and the prediction of future trends. Properly integrated into all departments of a business, an MIS can coordinate and enhance the channels of communication between departments and personnel that have experienced communication barriers in the past. An MIS can keep inventory, record sales, predict future sales, and then recommend how much stock should be ordered — based on the current inventory and the predicted sales trends.

If an MIS is such a wonderful thing, why doesn't every company have one? The fact of the matter is, many companies don't have an MIS system and many companies that make the attempt to implement one fail in that attempt. There are many reasons why companies do not wish to implement an MIS or have failed in their attempt to do so. Again, the reasons for this are a subject of much discussion and debate. While many critics try to blame first the managers and then the designers of the system, it is quite possible that the best explanation is that there is a problem with both the users and the designers.

The reason most often arrived at for the failure of an MIS system is lack of systematic use by the management. Change and progress are never completely easy or painless. It is a fact that most people do not wish to change established procedures and routines. It is also confusing and frightening to thrust forward into the rapidly changing mainstream of a technological business; keeping up with the new advancements in MIS is a huge task in itself. Comprehensive training and a well-organized "break-in" period should help to ease this shock of change and encourage the use of the MIS among managers. Another common problem with the implementation of a system is the lack of communication between the designers of the system and the managers who are going to be using it. If the system is not designed to meet the needs of the personnel using it, failure is virtually impossible to avoid. With careful communication between user and designer during the design phase, this problem can be circumvented. As you can see, an MIS is not without its problems, but with proper training and implementation, a manager will find the MIS one of his or her most valued tools.

BOOKKEEPING AND ACCOUNTING

The tasks of bookkeeping and accounting are, of course, based on mathematics. The first device that was made to aid in mathematics was the abacus. Basically just a frame with a series of small beads strung across, the abacus was used to speed up the mathematical manipulation of numbers. It was used before what we consider conventional bookkeeping or accounting was developed. The first instrument of the technological age of bookkeeping was probably the adding machine. With this machine, accountants were able to do their calculations on the ledgers more quickly and accurately. Advanced mathematics, such as calculus and abstract math, were aided by another device, the slide rule. Both of these tools, and those that evolved between them, were mechanical in nature.

Electronics entered this field with the invention of the computer. At first the computer had the same characteristics as the adding machine and performed only the most simple mathematical functions at a much slower rate than a person with an adding machine. Added to the speed problem of the computer was the space requirement. To perform the functions that can now be incorporated into a digital wristwatch, an early computer filled most of a floor of a building. Because of this, the computer remained the province of the scientist and the engineer for some time. After a while, though, advances in technology resulted in a reduction in the computer's size and an increase in the speed with which it performed mathematical functions. Today, calculators specially designed for the person who works in finances, bookkeeping, or accounting are available. With the touch of a button, an accountant can calculate interest on a loan, depreciation of an asset, bond yield to maturity and price, and perform the normal mathematical functions required to balance the books. One example of such a calculator is the HP-12C Programmable Financial Calculator shown in Figure 13-1.

The only disadvantage to using a calculator, for the accountant, is that all of the work must still be transferred to paper, by hand, just as it always has been. Although the calculator quickly gives him or her the correct answer, the accountant must still transfer all the intermediate-stage answers to the ledger form of the company's books. This intermediate transfer of answers is a slowing factor and the major drawback of the calculator. As you will see in the following paragraph, this is where computers and computer programs step in and make their greatest contributions.

With the advent of capable large computers, more or less reasonably sized, fully mechanized accounting became possible. These computers were programmed to accept numbers, in the same way that an accountant would enter them in the ledger, and then perform the necessary calculations and display the output in a column form, closely imitating the traditional method of bookkeeping. Some of the largest and most powerful computers could take this data and display it in graphic or chart form, to provide businesses with bar charts, pie charts, histograms, etc. These graphs could then be printed out and used as visual displays. The microcomputer is the machine that allowed companies of all sizes to computerize their bookkeeping and accounting systems. Relatively inexpensive and easy to use, microcomputers were ideal for companies too small to afford large computer systems. These new systems began incorporating fullscreen programs which implemented some of the most advanced ideas in bookkeeping and accounting. These programs allow the accountant to

Figure 13-1 HP-12C Programmable Financial Calculator (Courtesy of Hewlett-Packard Company)

move around the monitor screen and enter information as if the screen were an actual ledger sheet. The output from these programs can also be formatted as a ledger sheet or represented graphically. A more general form of bookkeeping and accounting programs that has become extremely popular is spreadsheets. They allow the user to build his or her own record or ledger sheet. This is most likely due to the success of Lotus Corporation's Lotus 1-2-3™ spreadsheet program. This program allows the arrangement of information by cells, which are specific locations labeled by a row and column number on the screen. The accountant/user can create sheets of any format he or she wishes. In addition, extensive calculation and graphics display abilities are at the user's disposal.

The current trend of bookkeeping and accounting systems towards smaller and easier-to-use systems will probably continue to have a great effect on businesses and their procedures in the future.

REPORT GENERATION

Report generation in business can usually be considered the orderly presentation of data and facts. Of course, as long as there have been organized businesses there have been reports. At first these were simply organized, handwritten displays of facts so that a superior could monitor crucial aspects of progress more easily. Later, when typewriters became standard office equipment, it was natural for reports to be produced with them. This eliminated the inconsistencies and deciphering problems that were inherent in handwritten reports.

With the introduction of computers able to store massive amounts of information, it was logical that someone should think of making the computer display its information in an organized form. This was the birth of

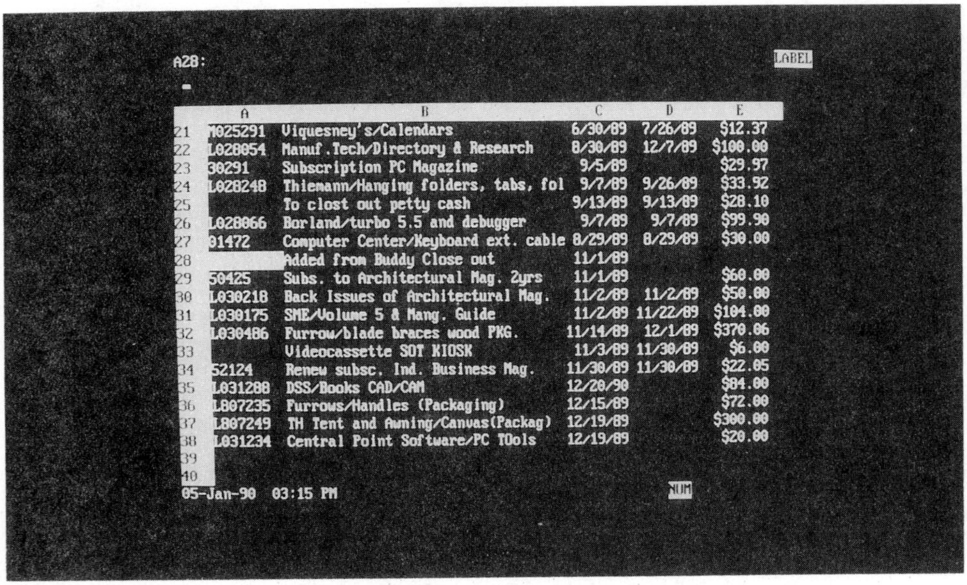

Figure 13-2   A Sample Lotus 1-2-3™ Spreadsheet (Copyright Lotus Development Corporation 1987. Used with permission.)

the report generator. Report generators can be defined as the program and/or hardware necessary for a computer to print out its information in a report form. The simplest hardware required for the computer to make reports is a printer of some sort. The first computer-generated reports were very simple. Lining up names, numbers, and other data into specified columns and rows on blank paper was the extent of a report generator's ability. Report generators have advanced considerably since their beginnings. They now work in two basic ways. The first method allows the operator of the report generator to use pre-printed forms that use information that the computer has stored. The second method allows the user to specify much more precisely where information is to be placed, and in what format, on the form to be completed.

Some problems accompany this method. The first is the difficulty for the user to specify where the information should go because the form requires the information in an exact location. The second problem is the cost involved in having special forms made up that the computer printer can use. Many printers can handle only a limited range of paper sizes and others require special holes or perforations on the sides of the forms to be printed. Some of the newest report generators were created to eliminate such problems. With the development of printers that could print graphics, as well as letters, report generators were able to allow the user to create the form that the information would be placed on. This was much easier for the operator of the computer because the form was designed at the same time that information was placed on it. In this way, the form could be designed to fit the information, instead of the information being adjusted to fit the available form. The cost of the forms also went down because the report generator could create forms on regular paper. Today, report generators are not usually a separate entity but rather part of an integrated data base package. Data base packages are software designed for the efficient storage, ordering, and display of information. Report generators provide the most flexible and powerful display methods, and for this reason they are usually included as part of a data base package.

A very popular data base package on the market today is Paradox, from Borland. This package combines all of the elements of a data base: organizing, storage, and display. With full-screen orientation for the input of information, this package allows the user to create a screen form that is extremely easy to use. The user presses special arrow keys to move around the screen, entering and correcting in any fashion that he or she might wish. Paradox also includes many features that allow users to organize their data however they desire. Advanced report generation is also supported in the program.

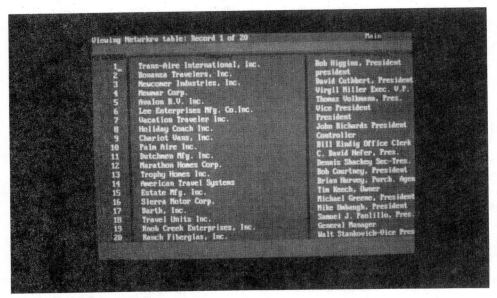

Figure 13-3 A Paradox Report

DESKTOP MANAGEMENT

Desktop management, or desktop organization, is also one of the most discussed topics and markets in the computer world today. Desktop organization began with devices that nearly all office personnel are familiar with or, in fact, still use today. The devices are items such as Rolodexes, address books, appointment calendars, and calculators; those things that average business people have on their desks in order to organize themselves and their work. Computers did not enter the field of desktop management until the introduction of the microcomputer into the business world. To be sure, there were address book programs, appointment programs, etc., on large mainframe computers but these were not desktop management. With the introduction of the microcomputer, a much greater number of employees in a business had access to all of the advantages a computer could supply.

Generally, a desktop organizer should have at least the minimum amount of useful abilities. What these are is a matter of what the user needs. The very basics that a desktop organizer should have are: a text editor (for short and easy memos), a simulated calculator, an address/phone book storage ability, and an appointment calendar service.

Some packages support more features, such as automatic phone dialing and alarm clock functions. In the past, such programs were written and worked well but were inconvenient to use. Users had to stop what they were doing, start up the desktop organizer, and then go back to what they were working on before. It was much simpler just to work with the traditional office tools found on the desk. In this way, users didn't have to stop what they were doing on the computer.

The software companies that were producing desktop organizers responded to this complaint by developing a method known as windowing. Windowing is the process of dividing up the computer monitor screen into well-bordered areas in which different tasks interact with the user. What was done was to have a desktop program that ran all the time off screen while other programs were being used. Users could work on various programs until there was need for the desktop program's abilities, at which time they could press a special "hot-key" combination. The desktop program would then open up a bordered window on the screen within which users could work. For example, a user might be calculating finances on spreadsheets when he or she receives notification of a future meeting that must be remembered. The user then presses a special hot-key combination and his or her desktop organizer places a window on the screen listing the available services. The user chooses the appointment service and stores the appointment information, then exits the desktop program and the window is closed. The user is now back in the spreadsheet program as if it had never been left.

Like all things, desktop organizers also have their problems. Since the desktop program must monitor the keyboard input at all times to watch for its hot key, it may end up fighting with other programs for control of the keyboard. The result of this struggle is likely to be the locking up of the computer keyboard, which would require the user to reset the computer system. This problem is being worked on and each succeeding generation of desktop programs comes closer to eliminating it entirely.

The computer's ability to run a desktop program all the time and still allow the use of other programs is a result of one of the most interesting techniques of programming today. This type of programming, known as memory-resident programming, is based on one relatively simple idea: leave the program installed, but inactive, in the computer's memory until it senses its hot key; then it begins to run. This is, in fact, just how the commercial desktop programs operate. When a user starts up the computer, he or she installs the program into memory. The program then begins watching the keyboard input that the user types in. If the key

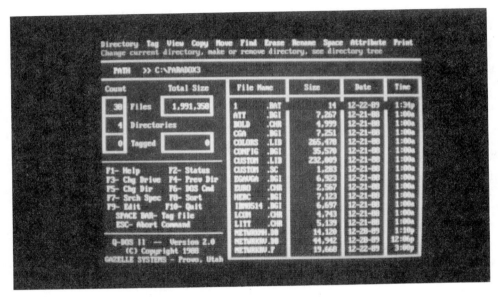

Figure 13-4   QDOS Screen

pressed is not the program's hot key, then it is simply passed along to the other program for which it was meant. If the key is indeed the program's hot key, then the program begins execution and opens a window to present the user with a complete list of all available options. This is the way memory-resident programs work.

One of the most popular desktop organizers is Sidekick™, by Borland International. Sidekick was one of the first programs to be memory-resident and window-oriented. Extremely popular, Sidekick has become the standard by which other desktop programs are measured. Sidekick has all of the basic functions of a desktop organizer along with an automatic phone dialer that works with a modem. What makes Sidekick stand out is its very fast speed, and its limited interference with other programs.

Even though the computer has taken over many of the functions that are vital to business, it hasn't yet reached the point where it can handle all of a business person's needs. Nevertheless, because of its speed and efficiency, the computer can boost the productivity of average business people by a considerable amount, provided that they know how to use it to their advantage. Computers in business have arrived and appear to be here to stay. The wise business person should at least be conversant with the basics of computer operation in order to keep up in this ever-developing field.

CHAPTER REVIEW

On a separate sheet of paper, write a response to each question, statement, or problem below.

Short Answer

1. What are management information systems?
2. List some applications of an MIS for the field of business.
3. Considering the need for decision-making in business, what is the disadvantage of an MIS?
4. What do the terms bookkeeping and accounting mean?
5. How do calculators help in bookkeeping and accounting?
6. What is the purpose of a Lotus 1-2-3™ spreadsheet program?
7. Describe at least two ways that report generators are used.
8. Briefly explain the Paradox package and its application.
9. Explain what desktop management is and how windowing applies to desktop management.

14

Medical Applications

INTRODUCTION

The advent of high technology has affected nearly all professional fields. Certainly, the field of medicine is not an exception; it has also been greatly improved by high tech. In order to provide you with some insight into state-of-the-art high tech medical equipment, a number of large hospitals, clinics, medical labs, and doctors' offices were studied to supply the information presented in this chapter.

DIAGNOSTIC EQUIPMENT

More than half of the sophisticated medical electronics equipment examined was used for finding out the condition of the patient. The following are some representative types of equipment.

High tech electronics was very apparent in the labs. There were blood test machines, drug analyzers, serum analyzers, blood gas machines, urine analyzers, protein analyzers, and a host of other equipment in use. A common, but highly technical, piece of equipment was the blood test machine. Coulter is one of the dominant manufacturers in this field. A typical Coulter blood analyzer can take a blood sample, test it, print out the data, store the data in its memory, and send the data to the hospital central data base all in less than a minute. The typical complete blood count (CBC) can be done in about five seconds. The machine actually identifies and counts the blood cells as they pass through a very tiny orifice; it also performs an analysis of the blood and arranges the collected data in a meaningful form. The longest part of the operation is the time it takes to print out the data on paper. There are many other machines of this type for all sorts of other tests.

Most of us are probably familiar with the X-ray machine, but advanced electronics combined with computer enhancement have significantly changed the kinds of pictures in use today. You may have heard of

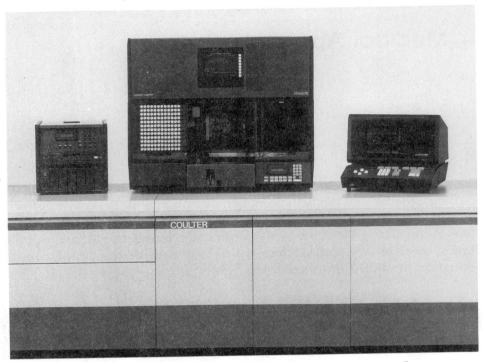

Figure 14-1   A Coulter Blood Analyzer (Courtesy of Coulter Electronics, Inc., Hialeah, FL)

the CAT scan; its new name is CT, the acronym for computer tomography (Figure 14-2). CTs are a highly sophisticated version of the basic X-ray machine. Like the X-ray machine, they emit a beam of electrons that goes through the body and strikes a film which captures an image of the body parts that it passed through. In CTs, the film is replaced by a detector that sends the images to the computer. The beam emitter and detector are contained in a doughnut-shaped enclosure that the patient is passed through. The CT system is rotated around the patient and a three dimensional picture can be formulated by organizing the data from the detector. The pictures can be focused, rotated, aimed at certain parts and slices of the body tissue, and then enhanced through the use of computer-imaging techniques. What all of this means is that if a person is suspected of having trouble with blood circulation in the head, a series of images can be generated to show the entire artery and vein structure in the areas affected. These images can be printed out or saved on floppy disks for future reference. The images provide the doctor with a three-dimensional

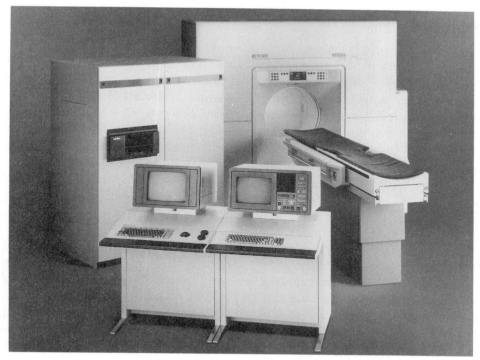

Figure 14-2   Picker CT Scan (Courtesy of Picker International, Charlotte, NC)

look inside the patient's head. This tremendous advance was made over the past few years.

Another interesting piece of diagnostic equipment is the Humphrey field analyzer. Accurately measuring a person's field of vision and the quality of vision at various angles is a tedious and time-consuming task. It is not unusual for a skilled technician to take thirty minutes to perform a comprehensive field analysis. Not only will the Humphrey machine do the test in less than ten minutes, but it also records the results on disk so that the patient's history can be traced and interpreted easily. The field analyzer flashes pinpoints of light on a background inside the machine. It continuously verifies that the patient maintains focus in the proper position by checking the blind spot to ensure that it has not moved. The machine can perform routine baseline tests or specialized tests for specific defects. The computer controls the testing procedure and performs record-keeping duties. The Humphrey field analyzer is a perfect example of the better care provided by diagnostic equipment created by advanced electronics.

PATIENT MONITORING

Patient monitoring is an area in which electronics has had a major impact. It is particularly useful when patients are in need of constant supervision. In intensive care units, coronary care units, and with other specialized types of care, constant monitoring is essential. Hewlett-Packard (HP) is a major manufacturer of patient monitoring equipment. The 78534 monitor/terminal is a good example of a high tech electronic monitor. The monitor can be used as a stand-alone unit or can be hooked into a local area network of monitors in an intensive care unit (Figure 14-3).

The HP monitor is capable of monitoring two temperatures, respiration, two EKGs, three invasive pressures, and one noninvasive pressure simultaneously. It keeps track of everything in real time but will also track long-term trends, watch for special events, print out strip charts, and display information from two patients on the screen at the same time, if needed. When connected into a network of monitors, patient information centers, data base computers, and network controllers, a small number of nurses can cover several critical care patients because they have accurate, real-time information available to them on command. This ensures that they are always attending to the patient who is most in need of care. Figure 14-4 is a typical intensive care unit (ICU) local area network.

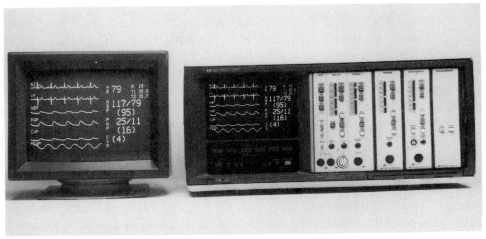

Figure 14-3   Hewlett-Packard Patient Monitoring Equipment (Courtesy of Hewlett-Packard Company)

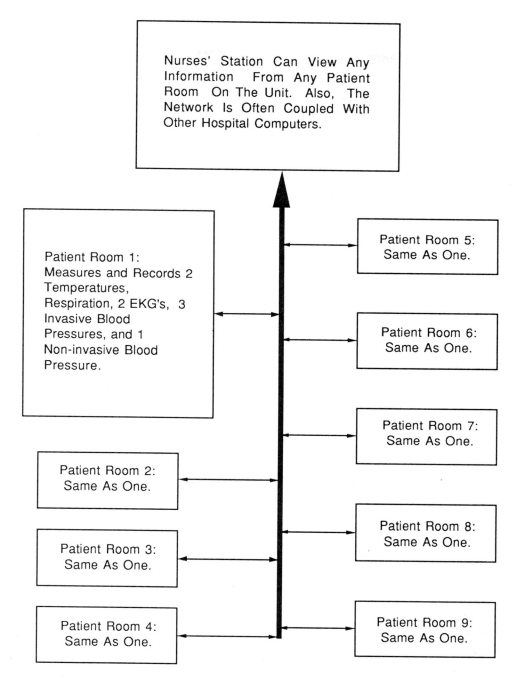

Figure 14-4 An ICU Local Area Network

OPERATIVE EQUIPMENT

As anyone knows who has been burned by an electrical shock, the wound does not bleed very much because the tissue is cauterized as it is damaged. Certain devices have been designed to do the same thing: solid-state electrosurgery devices are electronic scalpels. Using carefully controlled electrical energy, these probes cut through tissue and cause minimum bleeding. The problem is that the scar tissue from this procedure tends to heal slowly and therefore the equipment is used only in specific cases.

All sorts of electronic equipment have been designed for working on the patient. Fiber-optic lights can pass through small tubes to illuminate areas in the body for doctors to see. Defibrillators are the shock devices popular on television medical shows. They shock the heart into a rhythmic pattern and allow it to beat normally after it has lost its timing. There are also numerous special tools and devices that are used in microsurgery, such as precision laser scalpels for eye surgery. There is no doubt that modern electronics has had a significant effect on the types of tools that doctors and nurses use in their work.

MEDICAL RECORD KEEPING

All medical facilities of a significant size have computerized record keeping for patient records, billing, insurance form filing, and a host of other functions. The tasks are similar to those mentioned in the previous chapter's section on management information systems. Having our medical records available to the attending personnel at a moment's notice may prove to be a true lifesaver.

CHAPTER REVIEW

On a separate sheet of paper, write a response to each question, statement, or problem below.

Short Answer

1. List several electronic instruments or pieces of equipment that are used for diagnostic purposes.
2. Describe the function of a blood test machine.

3. What are the similarities and differences between an X-ray machine and a CAT scanner?

4. Describe how a field analyzer is used to measure a person's field of vision.

5. Explain the application of an HP patient monitoring system.

6. What is the advantage of using solid-state electrosurgery devices instead of ordinary scalpels?

7. Describe the purposes and advantages of medical record keeping.

15

Communications

INTRODUCTION

Communications is one of the major applications of electronics and computer technology. Today's world depends heavily on quick access to reliable and economical communication networks. Whenever information has to be transferred between men or machines, especially over long distances, a reliable communication system becomes vital. Common examples of electronic communication systems are the telephone, radio, and television. Other more specialized and sophisticated systems include live television coverage via satellite, mobile communications with cellular phone and paging systems, automated railroad systems operation, and aircraft and spacecraft guidance and navigation aids such as radar, sonar, or loran.

RADIO TRANSMISSION FUNDAMENTALS

The first things that come to mind when the subject of electronics arises are radio and television. This is true because these devices have had a great impact in our lives. To understand their operation, it is first necessary to gain some knowledge about wireless transmission. In broad terms, two main units constitute the basic communications system: the transmitter and the receiver.

THE TRANSMITTER

Before long-distance communication can be accomplished, it is necessary to convert the information into a form suitable for electronic transmission. This is done by converting the information to an electrical signal via a transducer, usually a microphone for voice information. Although this

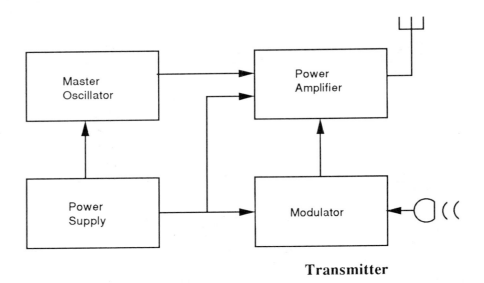

Transmitter

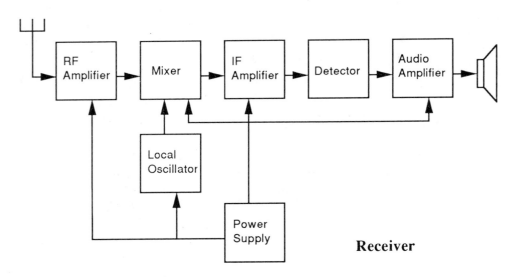

Receiver

Figure 15-1   A Basic Communications System

signal contains the information to be transmitted, it does not have enough
energy to travel through the air, due to its frequency and amplitude. To
make the signal suitable for radio transmission, it must be encoded into a
high-frequency signal, which has the form and energy to travel over long

distances. This high-frequency and high-power signal is called a carrier signal. In a sense, the signal containing the information rides on the carrier for its long-distance trip to the receiver. The process of encoding the information into the carrier is called modulation. The modulated signal that results from the process is routed to the antenna and transmitted through air or space in the form of electromagnetic waves. Even today, the ability of the carrier to travel over long distances through air or space remains somewhat mysterious. All you need to know, however, is that the carrier's ability to do this is based on electromagnetic principles.

THE RECEIVER

The receiver's job is to select the proper signal from the air, extract the information from the modulated wave, amplify it, and reproduce it as meaningful information. The process of separating the carrier from the signal containing the information is referred to as demodulation.

MODULATION TECHNIQUES

A number of different modulation techniques exist. Most common by far are two used by all commercial radio and television stations: amplitude modulation (AM) and frequency modulation (FM). At the transmitter, amplitude modulation is accomplished by using the voltage of the signal containing the information (modulating signal) to change the amplitude of the carrier, as in Figure 15-2a. The resulting signal has the information of the modulating signal encoded on its outer edges but also has the energy to travel over long distances. The AM radio band ranges from 525 to 1715 kHz. Frequency modulation is accomplished when the modulating signal is used to change the frequency of the carrier, as in Figure 15-2b. As you can see, in contrast to AM, the amplitude of the FM signal remains constant. The reason for this is that the information of the modulating signal is encoded in the variation of its frequency. The FM band ranges from 88 to 108 MHz.

Each type of modulation has its associated advantages and disadvantages. AM radio signals can reach out to longer distances than FM, but the amplitude-modulated signal is susceptible to noise and external interference. In contrast, FM signals, although they cover shorter distances than AM, have reduced static and interference and are suitable for high-fidelity, stereo-sound broadcasting.

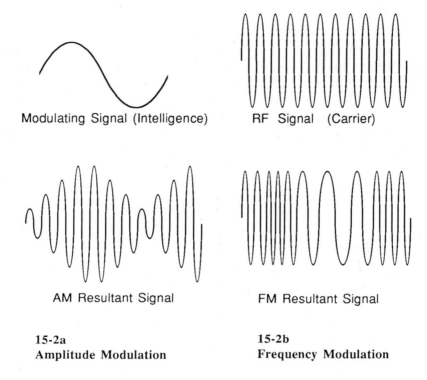

Modulating Signal (Intelligence)   RF Signal (Carrier)

AM Resultant Signal   FM Resultant Signal

15-2a
Amplitude Modulation

15-2b
Frequency Modulation

Figure 15-2 (a, b)   Modulation Types

Since commercial radio stations normally transmit only sound, one type of modulation is adequate to reproduce the transmitted information. There are times, however, when more than one type of information has to be transmitted. In this case, one type of modulation may not be adequate or practical to encode all the information into the signal. Multiple modulation of a signal is what makes television possible.

TELEVISION

A lot can be said about the technical aspects of television; from an electronics point of view, television appears to be a very complex device. Nevertheless, it can be reduced to functional blocks that constitute the television network system, as shown in Figure 15-3.

In simplified terms, the television transmitter can be thought of as a camera, an AM transmitter, and an FM transmitter integrated into one system. The receiver consists of an AM receiver, an FM receiver, and a

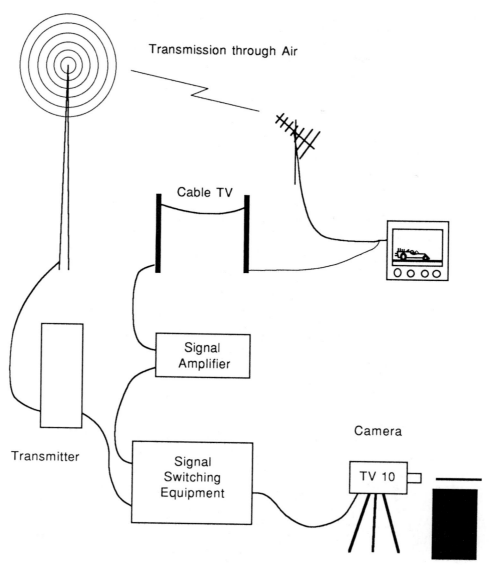

Figure 15-3   A Typical TV System

video monitor. The television signal is a composite signal containing many different types of information essential to the system. Sound is encoded into the signal through the frequency modulation process, and video information is encoded through amplitude modulation. The video portion of the signal includes a number of different bits of information, including luminance, color, sync, and blanking pulses that are used by the monitor to reproduce the picture. The different bits of information are extracted from the composite signal by special circuitry in the receiver. They are then used to produce individual signals, which, once amplified and conditioned properly, are used to drive the loudspeaker and the video monitor of the television set.

Television technology has developed slowly since the introduction of color. Solid-state electronics has replaced all of the tubes in the circuitry of today's TV, but the basic technology has remained the same. The change that is now sweeping the country is cable TV. It does not change the technology, but it does change the transmission medium. Instead of the signals being broadcast through the air and picked up by an antenna on the roof, the signals reach the television through a coaxial cable. The advantages of the cable system are improved picture quality and a greater number of available channels. With the old antenna system, it was necessary to buy a different antenna for each band of channels. They are all available on the cable.

Another factor that has increased the number of channels we can receive is the more frequent use of satellites in TV signal distribution. Many of the channels available on cable have been sent to the cable company by TV satellite. Homes with satellite TV receiver antennas can receive these channels without using any cable company. These developments have improved both our access to programming and the quality of the signal, but the real improvement in quality is just around the corner.

High-definition TV, or HDTV, provides a level of picture clarity that so far only the Japanese have managed to perfect. The problem with HDTV is that a signal broadcast in HDTV format cannot be shown on a regular set, and not only are HDTV sets few and far between, they are also very expensive. We therefore are not likely to see HDTV in the near future.

In the United States, however, developmental work is proceeding on digital TV. Instead of using analog signals to carry the signal, digital TV uses digital signals. These digital signals can be shown on any regular TV with the use of an adapter to convert the signals. Even though you don't get the benefit of higher quality, you can still see the picture. Both HDTV and digital signals are still undergoing development, but they will be available to us before the year 2000.

DATA COMMUNICATIONS

In a computer environment, it is often necessary to transmit data from one device to another. Communicating devices can be a fraction of an inch apart or thousands of miles away from each other. In some cases, the task is easily accomplished by sending digital pulses through wires connecting the communicating elements. For short distances this technique works well, but, as the distance between devices increases, the signal degenerates considerably. The wires become an antenna that receives electromagnetic interference from nearby electromagnetic fields (transformers, motors, power lines, etc.), making data transmission faulty or impossible. For this reason, a number of techniques have been developed to aid in long-distance data transmission. Before those techniques can be understood, it will be necessary for you to become familiar with some of the facts and terminology associated with the topic.

BAUD RATE

Baud rate is a measure of data transmission speed. It refers to the amount of digital information transmitted during a given time interval. Baud rate is defined as the number of signal changes per second and is commonly called bits per second.

MEDIUM

The medium is the physical part through which transmission takes place. A computer cable connecting two devices that are a few feet apart is an example of a medium. Computer cables that conform to industry interface standards, such as the RS-232C, can be up to 50 feet in length for transmission rates of up to 56,000 baud. Beyond 50 feet, data may be communicated successfully if the rate of transmission is reduced. Transmission through computer cable can be extended to up to 5,000 feet at 9,600 baud, with the use of amplifiers and signal conditioners that can reshape distorted digital pulses.

As transmission distances increase beyond 5,000 feet, transmission through computer cable becomes unreliable for digital signals. Nevertheless, the telephone company is willing to transmit data through the telephone line to almost anywhere in the world, but the form of the signal is changed to accommodate the long distances.

Other media suitable for data transmission are coaxial cable, fiber-optic cable, radio transceivers, and microwave transceivers. Coaxial cable is a metal conductor surrounded by a grounded, cylindrical foil shield. Although it is much more expensive to install than a telephone line, coaxial cable can transmit a much greater range of frequencies and can therefore accommodate much greater amounts of data.

Fiber-optic cable is made of a fine fiber of glass surrounded by a protective plastic coating. Information encoded into light can travel through glass fiber for a mile or so before the signal requires amplification and retransmission. Fiber optics can transmit an even greater amount of data than coaxial cables.

Radio transmission becomes an alternative when the use of a cable is impossible or when there are many receiving devices. Microwave transceivers are used to complement telephone or coaxial cable networks. They may also be used for intercontinental transmission applications via satellite.

A medium can be used to interconnect computer systems in a number of configurations. The communicating systems can be connected according to point-to-point, ring, star, multidrop, or hybrid configurations. Figure 15-4 shows the various types of pure networks. Each system has its pros and cons, but all have specific applications for which they are most appropriate.

The point-to-point configuration simply connects a transmission line between each computer system. This assures that each computer can talk to all others in the system. The design is simple to implement, but as the physical distance between the computers in the system increases, so does the cost of installation.

The ring configuration interconnects the communicating devices in a circular fashion. When any computer sends information, it includes the name or address of the intended recipient at the front of the message. Data are then passed around and checked by each member of the network until the destination computer is found, at which point the receiving computer takes the message out of the system.

The star network relies on a central computer, called the host, to receive data from the remote systems, to determine their destination, and to retransmit to the appropriate system. This host computer is used only as a network controller.

The multidrop configuration connects all communicating devices with a single line. When one system transmits, the rest listen to determine if the data are for them. The data are identified and received by the destination system, but they are disregarded by all other systems on the line.

Often the exclusive use of one configuration is not practical or feasible. In many cases, computers are connected in whatever way seems appropriate for the particular application. This kind of configuration is referred to as hybrid and is the most common arrangement.

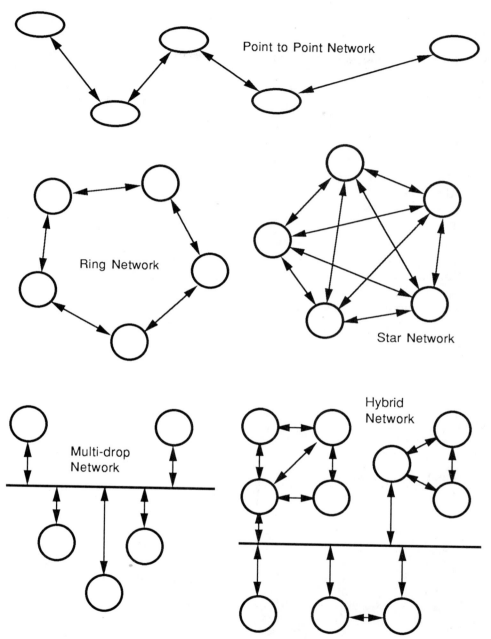

Figure 15-4   Computer Communication Networks

MODEMS

Although telephone lines are designed to accommodate voice signals and are not directly compatible for digital data transmission, the task can still be accomplished with modulation. During this process, the digital information is superimposed on a signal that is compatible with the medium. After the process of modulation is performed, the signal looks very much like the one carrying vocal information. This modulated signal can travel through the telephone switching networks. When it reaches its destination, it is restored to digital information by a reversing process called demodulation. A device capable of performing both modulation and demodulation is called a modem.

There are several ways of modulating data onto the carrier. The two most common for data transmission are frequency shift keying and phase shift keying. With frequency shift keying, data are transmitted by shifting between two frequencies. One frequency represents a zero, and a different frequency is used to represent a one. Phase shift keying uses one frequency to transmit both states. In this case zero is distinguished from one by a shift of the carrier's phase angle. Phase shift keying is difficult, but it is necessary for high-speed data transfer.

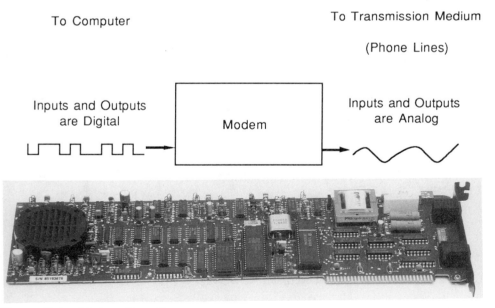

Figure 15-5   Modem Operation

PROTOCOL

Generally, protocol refers to the method used to transfer data. Protocol is the combination of all of the standards to be used in the data transmission and reception system. This includes everything from the modem to the type of software used to transfer data. The study of communication protocol is a course in itself.

One part of protocol is the type of data flow to be used during communication. Data may be transmitted in one direction only, in both directions simultaneously, or in one direction at a time. This is illustrated in Figure 15-6. When data always travel in one direction, it is said that the transmission line is operating in simplex. If data can travel in both directions simultaneously, the line is a full duplex loop. Finally, if data can travel in both directions, but not at the same time, the line is a half duplex loop. Full duplex modems are the most practical for use on switched telephone networks. All other types require dedicated lines. Dedicated or private lines are nondialed, high-speed data links connecting communication systems.

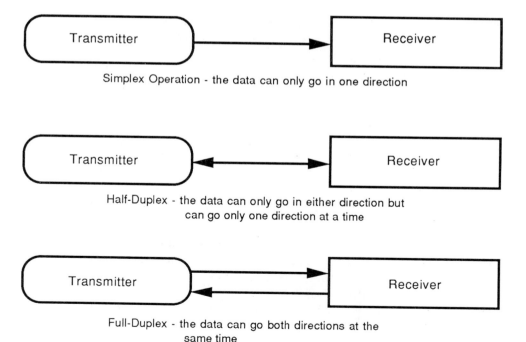

Simplex Operation - the data can only go in one direction

Half-Duplex - the data can only go in either direction but can go only one direction at a time

Full-Duplex - the data can go both directions at the same time

Figure 15-6   Communication Types

HIGH-SPEED DATA NETWORKS

As the need for data continues to grow in the business world, data communication methods are becoming more sophisticated. High-speed data networks can now route digital data around the world in a matter of seconds. From a computer in almost any city in the United States, you can use a modem and call up any of a dozen data networks that have access to the world and a lot of its data. You can log into any of a whole collection of data bases that contain information on business, education, medicine, the stock market, and a wide variety of other things. If you call from your home computer, you will probably use a low-speed line to access the information. If you work in an industry that uses data as one of its main resources, the computers will probably be connected to a high-speed network data link. This network may be a system that only company computers can use or it may be part of a larger system that connects to computers all over the country. Whether at home or at work, computers can tie you into the world at speeds we never thought possible.

Communications have come a long way from the Morse telegraph system to today's TV satellite system. The voice, music, pictures, and data can now be transmitted at phenomenal rates. It will be interesting to follow the technological developments in the communications field, and to watch the way our society, government, educational institutions, and other organizations react to and use each new capability.

CHAPTER REVIEW

On a separate sheet of paper, write a response to each question, statement, or problem below.

Short Answer

1. Why do audio signals need to be modulated before transmission?
2. Explain the process of modulating a carrier signal.
3. Describe the differences between AM and FM.
4. What is demodulation?
5. For television broadcasting, describe how audio and video information are transmitted.
6. What does baud rate mean?

7. List the different configurations in which communication systems can be connected.

8. Describe what a modem is and how it is used.

9. For communications protocol, list and describe the different types of data flow.

Fill in the Blank

1. The two main units that constitute a basic communication system are the _____ and _____.

2. A high-frequency and high-power signal that is used for transmission is called the _____ signal.

3. The process of encoding information into a carrier is called _____.

4. The process of separating the carrier from the signal containing the information is referred to as _____.

5. The television signal is a _____ signal containing different types of information.

6. Baud rate refers to the number of _____ per second.

7. With optical communication, the information is encoded into _____.

8. In communication protocol, when data travel in both directions, but not at the same time, the line is called a _____ _____ loop.

9. A device that is capable of performing both modulation and demodulation is called a _____.

16

Military Applications

INTRODUCTION

Military technology is probably the most advanced of all electronics applications. Research in communications systems, navigation systems, surveillance systems, guidance systems, weapons systems, and electronic countermeasures is some of the most sophisticated technology in existence.

COMMUNICATIONS AND CRYPTOGRAPHY

Communications was probably the first area in which electronics made its way into the battlefield. In conventional warfare, it is essential to be able to communicate with the various members of the team. Walkie-talkies, or portable two-way radios, revolutionized the effectiveness of the foot soldier because they ensured that he was in the right place and was striking at the right time. The walkie-talkie is still in use, as are an abundance of other devices and techniques for communicating on the battlefield. As military communications technology developed, longer distances could be covered with greater reliability. Figure 16-1 shows a transportable cellular telephone type of communications equipment in common use today.

While communication among the members of one side was important, it was just as important that the other side not understand what was being communicated. Cryptography solved this potential problem. Cryptographic equipment takes a normal message and encodes it for transmission in such a fashion that the opposing forces cannot understand the information. The intended receiver, on the other hand, can decode the transmission and obtain the original message. This is the same principle used by satellite TV companies to keep nonpaying viewers from receiving usable picture and sound. The military has dozens of cryptographic devices and each has a specific function. Some units are used with voice,

Figure 16-1   Communications Equipment (Courtesy of Motorola, Inc.)

some with low-speed data, some with high-speed data, some for analog information like TV signals, and some for highly secure communications. Of course, all of these devices are classified, but the principles of cryptography are common knowledge.

The science of cryptography is the study of encoding and decoding messages securely and quickly. This is usually done by sending a signal from an originating device, a teletype set, for instance, to a crypto transmitter. The transmitter scrambles (encodes) the message so that it sounds meaningless to a normal receiver, and the receiver at the other end unscrambles the information and sends it to another teletype set for the operator to read. The message is usually scrambled and unscrambled by the use of a code. This code tells the transmitter what to do to each bit of information to make it unintelligible to any device other than the receiver with the same code. This is analogous to writing a message and then converting each letter of the alphabet to its corresponding number, 1–26, and then adding 6 to each even number. The person to whom you had entrusted the code could figure out the message, but to anyone else it would look like a series of meaningless numbers. Crypto devices use a method similar to this. They take the incoming message and mix it with a separately generated signal to form a composite signal. This composite signal is then transmitted to the receiver and the same code signal is subtracted from the composite, leaving the original. Figure 16-2 is a block diagram of this procedure.

Cryptography works only if your opponents do not have your code and they cannot gain access to your machine to decode your messages. For this reason, machines and codes are closely guarded and codes are changed frequently.

RADAR AND SONAR

Radar is an acronym for *radio detection and ranging*. It is based on the principle that when a radio frequency signal encounters an object in air or space, that object reflects part of the energy that strikes it. A radar system transmits a pulse of energy and then it waits for any reflected energy to return from objects the pulse encounters. A basic radar system consists of a transmitter, a receiver, an antenna, a display unit, and a timing unit. The transmitter sends the pulse to the antenna, which transmits it in a particular direction. The reflected energy is received by the same antenna, but, because the transmitter is now off between pulses, the energy goes from the antenna to the receiver. The receiver processes the information and sends it to the display unit for viewing.

Since the transmitted pulse travels at the speed of light, if the time between the transmitted pulse and the received energy is measured and then divided in half (a round trip for the energy), the number of seconds

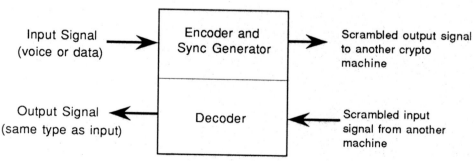

Figure 16-2 A Basic Crypto Machine

elapsed multiplied by the speed of light gives the distance of the object from the transmitter. The reflected energy indicates a presence (detection) and the elapsed time indicates distance (ranging).

There are, however, some other pieces of information that can be gathered from the returned energy. First, the amount of reflected energy indicates the size of the target. A blimp, for example, reflects more energy than a much smaller fighter aircraft. The position of the rotating antenna will let us know the direction of the target. Second, the receiver can gather additional information about the direction and speed of travel of the target if it contains a special part that utilizes the Doppler effect. The Doppler effect is a change occurring in the frequency of the reflected waves if the target is moving. The frequency of the returned energy will be higher if the object is headed toward the antenna, lower if the object is headed away, and the same if the distance between the object and the radar set is not changing. The amount of change in the frequency of the signal indicates the rate of speed of the object. Take a look at Figure 16-3. It represents all of this information in a more understandable manner.

Radars come in various types, depending on their intended use. These include air search, surface search, and tracking, among many other types of systems. An air search system looks for anything in the air. This is the type of radar found at airports for keeping track of air traffic. Surface search radar is usually used at sea or for other purposes aboard ship. It is used to keep track of other ships and coastlines. A tracking radar is used to pinpoint something in the sky and stay locked on it. It is often used to track a target, and relay position and speed information to the missile guidance system that we will discuss later.

A piece of equipment that is used with radar but is really communications equipment is called identification: friend or foe (IFF). The purpose of IFF is to identify an object that you cannot see or otherwise identify. It is used primarily in aircraft. IFF systems consist of a transponder (transmitter/responder) in the aircraft and a transmitter and receiver in a base unit or ship. When an aircraft is detected by the radar unit, the IFF transmitter sends out an interrogation signal. The airplane must receive this signal, decode it, and respond with the correct answer to properly identify itself. Figure 16-4 is a block diagram of an IFF system.

When the correct response is received by the base unit, a message is displayed on the radar screen to tell the operator that the plane has been identified as a friendly aircraft. If the correct response is not received, interceptor aircraft are usually sent out to greet the unidentified visitor. Again, the codes for the system are changed frequently to prevent the other side from deceiving the sender. If you can remember the time when

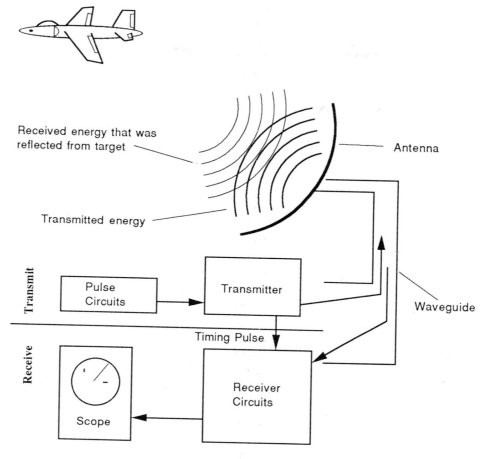

Received energy that was reflected from target

Antenna

Transmitted energy

Transmit

Pulse Circuits

Transmitter

Waveguide

Timing Pulse

Receive

Scope

Receiver Circuits

Figure 16-3   A Basic Radar Set

a U.S. warship accidentally shot down an Iranian passenger airliner, you may recall that the plane's IFF system had been modified. It was sending out a signal that should have been emitted only by a military aircraft. This confusion in the IFF system led to the ship's personnel making the wrong identification of the aircraft and deciding to shoot it down. It is clear from this example that IFF systems are potentially hazardous if not operated properly.

Sonar is similar to radar but has some significant differences. Sonar, *sound navigation* and *ranging*, has two methods of operation. Active sonar is used for underwater detection. The system contains a transmitter, a receiver, an antenna (called a hydrophone), and a display device. All of

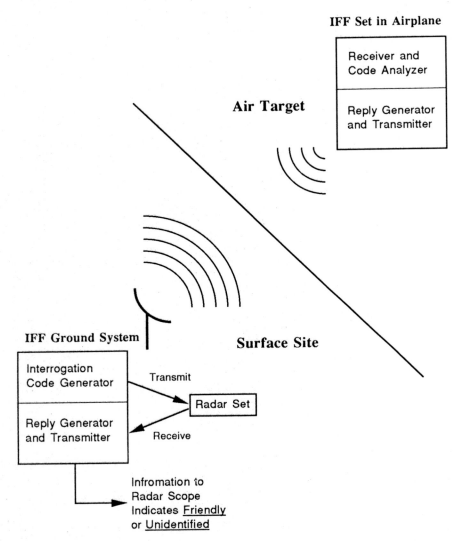

IFF Set in Airplane

| Receiver and Code Analyzer |
| Reply Generator and Transmitter |

Air Target

IFF Ground System

| Interrogation Code Generator |
| Reply Generator and Transmitter |

Transmit

Radar Set

Receive

Surface Site

Infromation to
Radar Scope
Indicates <u>Friendly</u>
or <u>Unidentified</u>

Figure 16-4   An IFF System

the principles used in sonar are similar to those of a radar system. The energy used for sonar is in the sound spectrum instead of the radio frequency range because sound travels very well in water. Figure 16-5 shows a basic active sonar system.

The other type of sonar is passive. This sonar receives only sound. The sound it listens for is transmitted by other vessels as they move through the water. Any vessel produces two types of sound when it moves. The first noise is called cavitation. This is caused by the

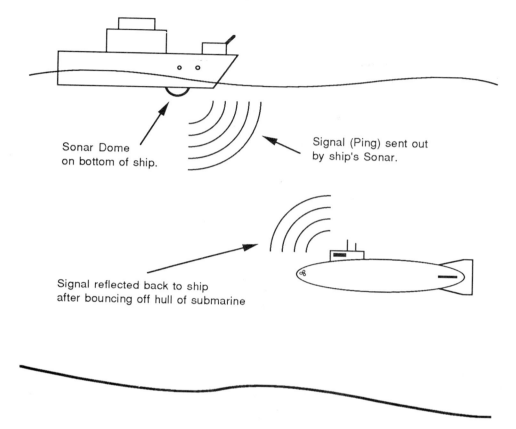

Figure 16-5   An Active Sonar System

disturbance in the water as the ship or submarine moves. The frequency and intensity of cavitation are dependent on the size and speed of the vessel. The other type of sound emitted is the mechanical noise of the vessel itself. Any machine has shafts, bearings, motors, and hundreds of other moving parts that cause noise. This noise is passed into the water and can be heard hundreds of miles away. By this method, the navies of the world can keep track of the movement of other nations' ships.

ELECTRONIC COUNTERMEASURES

Electronic countermeasures, or ECM, are used for misleading the other side's equipment. ECM is the practice of altering the signals that the receiver is processing so that the information is faulty. Jamming is a com-

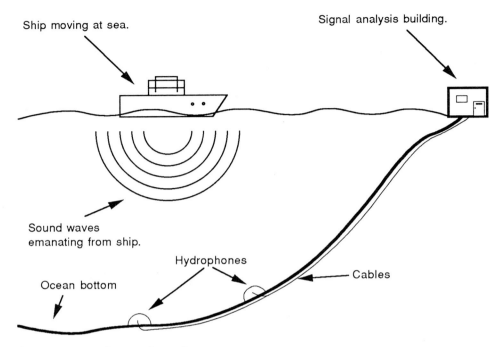

Figure 16-6 A Passive Sonar System

mon practice in ECM. To jam the receiver of the other party, a signal is transmitted in the same frequency but at a much higher power than the receiver is expecting. The information that the receiver needs is then lost or covered up by the high-power incoming signal.

The more sophisticated method of ECM is called false imaging. This is the practice of receiving the radar or other type of signal, analyzing it for frequency, power, pulse width, and other parameters, and then transmitting a false pulse back to the receiver in place of or in addition to the reflected pulse. This type of electronic gamesmanship can make a rowboat look like an aircraft carrier or make an aircraft appear to be traveling at mach 4 (twice the speed of sound). This type of electronic warfare is becoming very popular and very complex. Just think of the effect of making each of your ships look twice its size and three times as fast as it really is. The other end of this game is to make your vessel invisible. By masking or disguising the return pulse so the receiver does not process it properly, your ship can become transparent. You could also alter the return pulse so that the operator of the radar set would be convinced that his or her set was broken and that he or she could not rely on the readings. As you can see, the possibilities are endless, or so it seems from the defense budget.

GUIDANCE AND NAVIGATION

Guidance and navigation systems incorporate many types of equipment whose purpose is to tell you where you are and how to get where you want to go. Guidance systems are most commonly used with weapons systems. The guidance system is the electronics equipment that gets the missile to the target. Guidance systems fall into two categories, those that acquire the needed information to direct themselves to the target on their own and those that require external control signals.

The first group are the most complex and most expensive. A typical weapon of this type is the AIM-7 air-launched missile. This missile is told what target to hit and then is launched from the aircraft. The missile's system finds the target with its own radar and flies directly to it. This missile will find its target even if the aircraft is destroyed after the missile's launch. An AIM-9 missile will find the target on its own also but it must be pointed in the right direction before it is fired. The AIM-9 homes in on the heat produced by the enemy aircraft's jet engine.

The other type of weapon is one that flies to the target but is in need of guidance by the launching vessel. Some missiles that are launched by ships are guided by radio signals from the ship relayed by the radar that is tracking the target. Figure 16-7 shows this type of system.

Missiles that have their own guidance system and must travel thousands of miles to their target (like ICBMs) need an accurate system for keeping track of where they are. This is almost a navigation system. A navigation system determines where an object is with relation to the earth. Using a magnetic compass to find your way through the woods is employing a crude navigation system. With the development of nuclear-powered submarines that stay submerged continuously for many months, systems had to be developed so that the sub knew exactly where it was at all times. If the sub was going to launch missiles at the enemy, it had to have precise information to feed into the missiles' guidance system so that they headed for the enemy and not for home.

A system called loran is used extensively in this country for the navigation of ships. Loran uses a network of transmitters scattered around the country's coasts as its basis. Each of these transmitters sends out signals that are unique and identifiable. A ship with a loran receiver picks up these signals and can quickly tell its location. Loran has grown into the most widely implemented system in the world and is used for private navigation and general aviation as well as for military purposes.

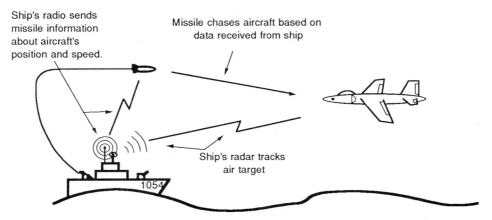

Ship's radio sends missile information about aircraft's position and speed.

Missile chases aircraft based on data received from ship

Ship's radar tracks air target

1054

Figure 16-7 A Guided Missile

STAR WARS

The Strategic Defense Initiative (SDI) is commonly known as star wars technology. It is actually a set of satellites that are intended to protect the United States from attack by high-flying missiles or other satellites. The system is a combination of tracking, identification, communication, and laser weaponry equipment. The satellites are designed to detect enemy satellites or missiles, track them with pinpoint accuracy, and use a high-power laser beam to destroy them. This kind of system is extremely complex and expensive, and for these and other reasons has caused a lot of controversy. However, we're sure to hear more about this system and others like it well into the next century.

CHAPTER REVIEW

On a separate sheet of paper, write a response to each question, statement, or problem below.

Short Answer

1. What is cryptography? Describe some applications for it.
2. Explain the principle of a radar system. List some applications for it.

3. How are the direction, the distance, and the speed of a moving object determined by using radar?
4. Classify several types of radar and their uses.
5. Explain the operation of an IFF.
6. Describe the basic difference between sonar and radar.
7. Why is sonar preferred in underwater detection?
8. What is the purpose of a guidance system?
9. Identify two types of guidance systems.

Fill in the Blank

1. In cryptographic transmission, the normal message is _____ before transmission and needs to be _____ after reception.
2. A basic radar system consists of a _____, a _____, an _____, a _____, and a _____.
3. The principle used to find the speed and direction of a moving target in radar systems based on the frequency of the reflected wave is called _____ _____.
4. IFF is an abbreviation for _____ _____ _____.
5. The antenna used in a sonar system is called a _____.
6. To jam a receiver, a signal of the same _____ is transmitted with a very high _____.

17

Home and Personal Uses

INTRODUCTION

In the course of technological development, several inventions have had major impacts on society. Electricity, the automobile, the airplane, television, and the hand-held calculator are some that come to mind. Another invention that is finding its way into society is the personal computer, or PC. These smaller cousins of the mammoth computers, used in universities and labs, have found their way into our offices and homes at a staggering rate. But what exactly is the personal computer? What can it do for us and how does it affect the way we live? These questions deserve serious thought.

PERSONAL COMPUTERS

What is a personal computer? Most people tend to think of a personal computer as a computing machine that they have at home or at the office. For our purposes, we will define the term personal computer in the following way. Personal computers share a variety of common characteristics that include compact size, single-user operation, and close proximity of the pieces of the system. Personal computers are generally small enough to be put comfortably on the top of a desk, but they can also be portable, briefcase size, or even small enough to fit into your pocket. Single-user operation means that only one person at a time can use a personal computer. This is a major difference between personal computers and the larger, mainframe computers. Mainframe computers can be used by several people at once without any noticeable slowdown in operation. The last trait that is really unique to personal computers is their completeness as a unit. When you sit down in front of a personal computer, you have all the parts of the computer right there in front of you. The personal computer system includes the keyboard, system unit, and monitor; in

Figure 17-1   Typical PC System (Courtesy of International Business Machines Corp.)

other words, it contains all of the necessary components of a computer system.

When you work on a mainframe, you usually sit in front of just a monitor and keyboard. The system unit is normally large and situated in an environmentally controlled room.

There are other parts common to most personal computers, even though they are not required for use. Tape and disk drives are used to store programs and information permanently, and printers are used to print papers, reports, or graphics. Modems are devices that allow a personal computer to use the phone lines to communicate with other personal computers or mainframe computers.

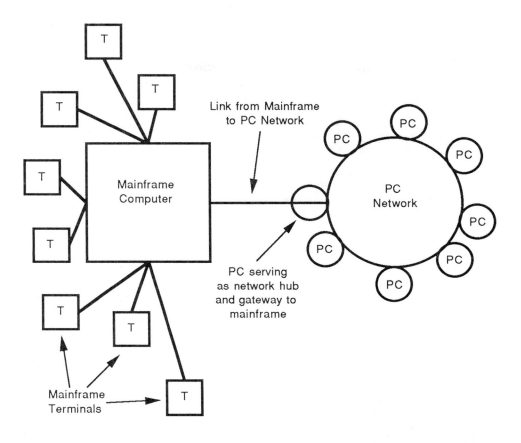

Figure 17-2   Mainframe Environment and PC in Office (Courtesy of International Business Machines Corp.)

But why are personal computers so popular and why are they popping up in so many parts of our lives? The most obvious reason is that one no longer had to be a computer scientist or an engineer to use a computer. As the first personal computers gained acceptance, especially those manufactured by the Apple Company, they began to make their way into the home. With the availability of prewritten software (computer programs), the early Apples really became very popular. When IBM's personal computer entered the market, no one was prepared for the level of acceptance it gained. With hundreds of companies and individuals writing programs to be used on the IBM PC, it grew to dominate the market and created a standard for the personal computer. In the current market, IBM computers and IBM-compatible computers still dominate sales. Today, literally hundreds of ready-to-run programs of many kinds can be bought for personal computers. Everything from programming languages to games is available to the personal computer owner. Word processors for report writing, home budget programs, recipe filing systems, and appointment calendars are just a few examples of the programs marketed for the PC.

HOUSEHOLD AUTOMATION

Household automation, the running of a house automatically under computer control, has been a favorite subject of science fiction writers for many years. Just as stories were written about man walking on the moon years before it actually happened, household automation has also become a reality.

The center of a household automation system is, not surprisingly, a personal computer. A personal computer can be connected by means of special devices to the outlets and switches of your house to automatically perform many tasks. Imagine yourself getting up in the morning and walking into your kitchen. You used the home control program on your computer to turn on your coffee pot about fifteen minutes ago and now you can sit down to your coffee right away. Looking outside, you see that the sprinkler system has come on and watered your grass during the night. When you are ready to leave for work, you instruct the computer to turn on the alarm system for the day and to check all appliances and lights in the house, turning them off if you have forgotten to do so. This may sound far-fetched, but the technology for this sort of household control is available today. Nevertheless, most household automation includes only security systems and the timed and remote control of the home's

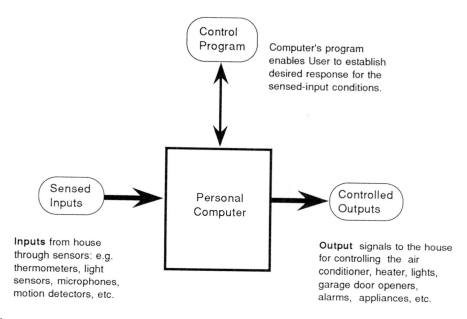

Figure 17-3   The Personal Computer in Household Automation

electrical system. In other words, it is very easy for the computer to turn things on or off. Lights, appliances, electronic garage doors, etc., are the limits of affordable control by today's personal computer.

Another type of automation being developed for homes is the ability to turn lights on when a person is in the room and then turn them off when the person leaves. This has been attempted with photo sensors at the door to turn the light on when a person enters the room and turn them off again when that person leaves. This has not quite been perfected; when a second person enters the room the lights go out. Other attempts have been made to set the lights to turn on or off at a certain level of noise. In this way a person could walk into a room and clap his or her hands for the lights to turn on or off. The problem with this is that any loud noise would do. If you have children, the lights may go on and off quite often. A new version of this technology turns on the lights for a preset amount of time after any noise. Each noise resets the timer, so if you were in the room with the TV on, the lights would stay on until the room was silent for the length of time set on the timer.

The future of household automation holds many exciting advancements. Voice recognition, voice control, and speech synthesis are among some of the leading areas of development today. These technologies are now in their infancy, but, as they develop, they will make marvelous additions to our household control systems. Soon we will be able to ask the house to turn off or on the lights and the stereo, and the house will be able to talk back to us (we hope not like our kids). Although these technologies are still in the developmental stages, their contributions to household automation are not too many years away. Today's speech synthesis is somewhat computer-like and voice control involves learning a certain way to speak in order for the computer to understand you.

Robotics is another field that is having an impact on household management. The garage door opener is an application of a simple robot. Today, robots are used to open doors and do other simple tasks. In the future, though, robots may be the maid and butler of the family, cleaning and maintaining the home under the direction of the computer.

IMPACT ON QUALITY OF LIFE

How do computers affect the way we live? One could answer that the computer has affected us in many ways, some subtle and some obvious. Most financial records of your personal affairs are kept and managed by computer. Computers are used by our banks, schools, businesses, and even the corner grocery store.

One way, then, that computers affect our lives is in how we do our business. With computers we can conduct our affairs with more accuracy (most of the time) and more speed. The price tag scanners at the grocery store help the cashier total our charges faster and produce an itemized printout of our purchases. The computer at the bank helps the teller make a quick and accurate transaction for us. These are things that most people interact with on a daily basis.

Another field in which computers affect our lives is that of medicine. Most hospitals have computers and networks to transfer information anywhere in the world. Computers aid in medical research and in complicated surgery. Lives can be saved because patient records can be transferred from one doctor to another hospital in a medical emergency.

But what about the personal computer at home? The difference here is the fact that the personal computer has not become a standard item in every household. Despite their dropping prices, computers remain beyond the reach of many. For those who do have computers, the effect that the computer will have on their quality of life is dependent on how much they are willing to learn about it and how much of their routine they allow the computer to take over. For those who desire, the computer can be a window to the world. The PC user can shop from his or her computer console, choosing the items and indicating the point of delivery. The charges for the items are also taken care of by computer, which records them against a credit card or bank account. Of course, this is a simplified description. You would need some way of communicating with another computer in order to complete your transaction. As we have discussed, this is usually done with a modem.

Computers can also improve our lives by allowing us more leisure time. The computer can help us accomplish our tasks faster, thus allowing us time to pursue other interests. How much a computer can help you is determined by how much effort you are willing to expend learning to use it. Using a word processor can shorten the time that it takes to write a book report or an office brief, but you must be willing to spend the time to learn how to do these things efficiently. Too many people who begin to learn about personal computers throw up their hands and quit because of the frustration involved in dealing with something unfamiliar and complex. In these cases, the computer becomes an expensive mistake, of no use to anyone; but for those who have patience and willingness to learn, this situation is an exception rather than the rule.

How will computers affect our lives in the future? Two basic views are held. One predicts that we will someday create a computer that is too smart, that is capable of human thought or response. This view is supported by the work done in artificial intelligence. Consider, however, our discussions of the disadvantages and shortcomings of computers. Despite all their advantages, the limitations of computers are many, and it is therefore unlikely that we will be "taken over" by them.

The other view holds that the computer is a tool and that, as such, it will continue to improve, becoming more versatile and capable. Computers have found their way into elementary school systems and are being carefully integrated into various areas of the school curriculum. The next generation will grow up with computers, learning and mastering them, in addition to their normal education, in the same way that the previous generation mastered reading, writing, and arithmetic. Even our telephones are computerized now, with a host of new services. Someday most homes may have a visual phone so that you can see the person you are speaking to. With information about the groceries that you bought and nutritional habits, in addition to your own traditional recipes, the computer may become the meal planner of the household. The possibilities are only as limited as our imaginations.

Of course, the computer is not the only electronic instrument in our homes. Alarm clocks, timers, TV's, radios, microwave ovens, kitchen appliances, razors, water sprinklers, automatic lights, security systems, thermostats, and so on are all now available to American consumers. These devices have made our lives better, perhaps, but not simpler. Our VCR needs programming, our two-person, two-station alarm needs to be reset, and how do we cope when the power goes off? Everything in the house blinks when the power comes back on and it seems as if every appliance must be reinstructed how to function properly. These problems will go away eventually, but they will probably be replaced by more sophisticated problems, like robots that do the wash but forget the bleach in the white load, etc. Your only hope is to learn more about these devices so that you can troubleshoot, repair, and modify.

SUPERCONDUCTIVITY

An area of intense research that has not been mentioned thus far and that has the potential to dramatically alter our lives is superconductivity. It has been around for years but has not found practical applications outside the laboratory. Superconductivity is the ability of materials to conduct electricity without resistance. In the early chapters of this book, we learned that all materials have some resistance. In the field of superconducting, the resistance of the material is negligible. This phenomenon was discovered in 1911 but has remained relatively obscure until recently because materials could only be made to superconduct at temperatures close to 0 degrees Kelvin. If you are familiar with the Kelvin scale, you know that this is –273 degrees on the Celsius scale. At such an extremely cold temperature, it is no wonder that to this point superconductivity has been of no real value. But recently, experiments in high-temperature superconductivity have been successful. If materials could be made to superconduct at normal atmospheric temperatures, electricity and electronics would be revolutionized. Conductors would no longer generate any heat. The electric service to our houses could be run with tiny wires. The field as we know it would never be the same again. But these changes may not happen soon. Remember how nuclear power was going to make electricity so cheap that our electric bill would be pennies a month? It's easy to get overexcited about the potential of new technology, but it's still nice to know what developments are being worked on in the labs and what potential they hold for our lives.

Finally, some thoughts that should be considered in the midst of all the computerization and automation of today's society: As has been mentioned before, the computer can assume responsibility only for the tasks that we delegate to it. We must remember that a computer is only a machine, no matter how wonderful it can appear. We have a responsibility to consider carefully what we allow computers to do for us. Computers, and all advanced technology, should be used to help us, to allow us more time to create a better world; they should not be used as an escape from our responsibilities, or as a way to avoid doing the right thing.

CHAPTER REVIEW

On a separate sheet of paper, write a response to each question, statement, or problem below.

Short Answer

1. What is the difference between a mainframe and a personal computer?

2. What are the three basic units that constitute a personal computer?

3. List several software packages that are available for a household PC.

4. Use block diagrams to prepare your design for a computerized home.

5. How can robots be used to improve our lives?

18

Applications in Education and Training

INTRODUCTION

For many years, computers and electronics have been working their way into the methods by which we learn. But recently, with the introduction of the microcomputer, their impact on learning has been significant. As we discussed in the chapters about computers, for a long time computing machines were very big and extremely expensive. Applications for education and training were developed but they were limited to large companies or organizations with large budgets that could finance the necessary computer power.

EARLY EFFORTS

The development of radio and television, and the subsequent advancements in film, videotape, and audiotape, provided the first real applications of electronics in education and training. These media have been around for many years and continue to be popular. With the development and popularization of the home VCR, the use and distribution of videotapes have taken on a whole new dimension. From golf to auto repair to physics to flower arranging, if you need to learn some information or skill, you can probably find a tape that will claim it can teach you. We've watched several golf instructional tapes and our game hasn't improved much, but the problem may be with our ability to implement the information presented, not with the information itself.

Video- and audiotapes are fine for some types of learning, but they do not allow for much interaction. These media present the material in a linear fashion; that is, the tape starts, proceeds in the order the material is put on the tape, and finishes when the tape is over. This is fine if the learner remains at the level of the material on the tape, if he or she can follow the order of the material, and keep up with the speed of presentation. But when one part is covered too fast or is not understood by the learner, confusion sets in and the rest of the session may not be very effective. The program or material cannot react to or be tailored to the requirements (basic ability, learning speed, learning style, background, and experience) of the learner. Of course, one can use pause, fast forward, and rewind on a VCR, but the learner has to control the program and the time required to rewind in order to review previous material may be bothersome.

THE COMPUTER TUTOR

What we need is some way to present video, graphics, and audio information at the proper level and speed, and in the proper order, for each individual learner. These requirements are met in a tutorial situation — one teacher and one student. The teacher presents the material and constantly evaluates the progress of the student to determine the style, order, and speed of presentation, as well as the need for more fundamental instruction. Researchers in the field of computer-based training have been trying to perfect the "computer tutor" for many years.

The early computer-based training systems were developed on mainframe computers. This severely limited their application because of the expense of the systems, and even though these were the biggest computers of their time, they were not fast enough to process all the data needed to deliver instructional material, receive input, analyze the situation, and implement program instructions based on the progress of the student. Another drawback to the early systems was the method by which the courses were created. There was no special software available to help a course developer write the code to implement the course, so it had to be written in a source language like FORTRAN, C, Basic, etc. This required the teacher/course developer to also be a programmer, or to work closely with a programmer to prepare the instruction.

CBT SYSTEMS

The developments of the past five to ten years have drastically changed the potential and utility of computer-based training applications. Today, computer-based training (CBT) systems can be found in many configurations and applications. From kindergartners to jet pilots, people are using computers to help them learn. Very few mainframes are used today for training applications. Most programs are developed for microcomputer delivery; however, some are written for minicomputer systems. Most minicomputer applications are developed for multiuser environments; that is, many people can take training on the same system at the same time. Most micro system applications are intended for one learner at a time.

A typical microcomputer teaching system has the following capabilities. It has a microcomputer at the heart of the configuration, running system and application software and managing the instruction. It sends information to the user through the screen, speaker, and other output devices. It receives inputs from the learner through the keyboard, joystick, mouse, touchscreen, microphone, or any of a variety of devices. It also maintains records of instruction and student performance.

The management of the instruction is where most of the computing power is necessary. After the system has been booted, a course typically starts automatically. The software will ask the student if he or she has ever used the system before. If not, some basic introduction will be provided. If the student has experience with the system, he or she will then be asked if he or she would like to start at the beginning of the lesson or pick up where the last session ended. The program directs the system to the appropriate position and begins instruction.

SOFTWARE DEVELOPMENT

Most computer instruction consists of providing information, asking questions or getting some type of feedback from the learner, matching up learner performance against program rules or guidelines, and controlling the delivery of material to the learner. How does a course developer go about writing a program for such a course? In most cases he or she will use a specific type of application software called Authoring Systems. An authoring system is just like a word processor, except that a word processor's goal is to produce documents and an authoring system's purpose is to assist in the development of courseware (a new word for a software course). Typical authoring systems will interface and manage the input and output devices, provide an easy method to input the information into the course, allow the author to define the structure of the lesson, including the performance requirements and the paths of remediation, and keep student records. Authoring systems cost from a few hundred to several thousand dollars and run from rather simple to very complicated.

Typically, there is a trade-off between power and complexity. The more powerful and flexible a system is, the more difficult it is to learn to operate and the more it costs. TenCore, CDS Genesis, Course Builder, and Best Course of Action are a few of the popular authoring system packages available today for microcomputer instruction development and delivery.

HARDWARE

All computer-based instructional delivery systems have a computer in them somewhere. Many use standard PCs like the Macintosh and the IBM-PC as the manager of the system. Most configurations use special peripherals (e.g., audio-video simulator, touchscreen mouse, keyboard, etc.), specifically designed for training applications. In a well-developed CBT application, the peripherals used will be selected based on the target audience. If training is being developed for secretaries, the peripheral chosen as the main source of input would be the keyboard since the target audience would be expected to be comfortable with that device. If, however, a driver training simulator was being developed, the best approach would probably be to hook the computer up to a mock-up of a car driver's seat so that all the controls would look and act as they would in a real situation.

This brings up the question of the quality of CBT and computer simulators. Are they any good? The answer is that, in most cases, they are as effective as we make them. An example of this comes from the airline industry. For most commercial pilots, the first time they actually fly a 747 it is full of passengers. On his or her first time in command of the jumbo airplane, the pilot has to contend not only with all the technology of the aircraft, but also with the knowledge that there is a planeload of passengers depending on him or her. Simulators in the airline and aviation industry have developed to the point that in many ways they are better than the real planes for training and instruction. The performance and "feel" of the simulator are indistinguishable from those of the actual aircraft and allow the pilot to experience many more situations than he or she would want to with passengers aboard. There is no doubt that computer-controlled simulators have improved the airline industry.

Another question is, which input devices are best for a regular computer? Should we be using a mouse, a keyboard, a joystick, a trackball, a touchscreen, or some other device as our standard interface? The answer to that question is not clear. Currently, a rule of thumb is to use the device that is most appropriate for the target audience and the material to be delivered. You will therefore see a variety of systems all claiming to be the best, based on their user interface. The way to decide for yourself is to try them out and judge them by the same set of measures.

Now a little about output devices. Many computer-based training systems use the typical computer screen and graphics for visual output and the sounds the computer can make as audio output. Today's technology, however, allows us to expand considerably on this capability. The three main areas of systems enhancement are the improvement of computer graphics, the addition of TV-quality video to the system, and the use of natural audio, that is, sounds just as we hear them, including natural speech. Utilizing commercially available hardware and software to include these advancements can greatly improve the usefulness and capability of a system.

Computer graphics have progressed significantly in recent years. Monitors the size of typical TV screens now have the resolution to produce images that very closely approximate a TV picture. In fact, the newest equipment provides computer graphics of TV quality. A new field, digital video, is emerging that gives us the ability to watch TV on our computer. Digital video is the process of taking a typical TV signal (NTSC, if you remember from previous discussion), converting it into a digital signal, and displaying it on a computer monitor at the same quality level as our TV, if the computer graphics systems is good enough. With digital video, we can freeze a frame, capture it into our favorite graphics program, and modify it. The modified image can then be used in a computer-based training application. Think of the potential uses. If, for example, you were taking a course on bowling, and you were looking at a video instruction sequence but at a specific moment needed more detail and explanation, you could stop the video and details and explanations would be frozen on the screen. Digital video also eliminates the flicker you see when you pause your home VCR. If there is any movement on the screen when you hit pause, you will notice a jitter in the picture. Digital video eliminates this jitter because you are not looking at an NTSC signal but at a digital picture, which, as you remember from previous discussion, is a single screen full of pixels.

VIDEODISC PLAYERS

This next section will address the problem of getting to an exact spot on a videotape without fast forward and rewind taking too much time. Let's look at an example from audio. For some time now, cassette tapes have been used for audio recording. When we wanted to hear a specific song, or more specifically, a particular part of a song, we had to spend a few minutes pushing the fast forward and rewind buttons. The arrival of the compact disc, or CD, changed that. Now we can go directly to the song we want; however, we still have a little trouble getting to a certain place in a song. A similar development has taken place in the video industry, but with even more capability. The video disc. The videodisc is like a music CD. Information is stored on the disc in the same way and they even look alike.

There are two types of videodiscs; they differ in the way they have the information recorded or formatted on the disc. A CLV (constant linear velocity) disc is very similar to the music CD. You can go to some places very quickly but you cannot go to any specific spot on the disc on demand. A CAV (constant angular velocity) disc solves that problem. On a CAV disc, you can go directly to any frame on the disc in less than half a second. This capability, combined with the digital video discussed earlier, has great potential for education and training. Now we can put video instruction on a disc instead of a tape, hook the disc player to a computer, watch the video on the computer screen during the instruction, and when we forget something we saw earlier and need to review, we can go directly to the previous video with no noticeable wait. This gives the course developer tremendous advantages when a student needs remediation on a topic. The student can be branched into a review segment and may not even know that he or she is reviewing previous material.

DIGITAL AUDIO

Videodiscs solve the picture problem, but how do we make these computer systems sound normal? Of course, an audiotape player could be attached and controlled by the computer, but the problems of getting to the right spot at the right time would persist. The obvious solution might be to use a CD player. The problem here is that the computer needs to find the audio fast and also find the exact audio needed for the current instruction. The format of a CD does not allow for precise location of audio information. In fact, no commercially available sources of audio information have the combination of sub-second access time and precise addressability.

The solution to this problem comes in two forms. The first solution is to put the audio on the videodisc with the video. Whenever a linear segment is being retrieved from the videodisc, two audio tracks are available for use by the system. The two tracks can be used for stereo or can be used independently. It is possible to use the same video in two different places in the course by using different audio tracks. This is a good solution for situations where full-motion video is being used, but what about audio for the times when the course developer needs to use a single frame, like a still picture? When this happens, the videodisc player shows the same frame over and over. In this case it is not possible to use audio off the videodisc; as we have already discussed, tape players and CDs are not up to the task. Digital audio, however, is. You may have seen some devices that use digital audio. There are some new telephone answering machines that have the announcement message stored in RAM and record callers' messages on a tape. The announcement message is an application of digital audio. When an announcement message is recorded, instead of the message going onto tape, as in most machines, the words are sampled by the digital audio recording electronics and the samples are stored in memory in the answering machine. When someone calls and the machine activates, the samples are retrieved from memory and played back. The voice sounds just like that of the person who recorded it. In fact, the quality in many cases is better than that of taped messages. New digital message telephone systems use the same technology.

This solves the problem of making the computer sound real, but what about access time and pinpoint data retrievability? When one of these digital recordings is made, a file name is given to the collection of samples. It is the same kind of name given to any other file the computer uses. When a specific piece of audio is needed, the computer simply calls up the file and sends it to the digital audio electronics that turn it into real speech and send it to the speaker. These audio files can be stored on the computer's hard drive or on an external drive, such as a CD-ROM. An excellent demonstration of digital audio is available from a MacRecorder (a $150 device that includes software) and a Macintosh computer.

THE FUTURE OF CBT SYSTEMS

When we combine all of the new technologies available, we begin to see the emergence of computer-based training platforms (the hardware required for a complete system, e.g., the control computer, input/output devices, memory tape, etc.) and interactive videodisc training systems that have great power and flexibility. When the course developer uses one of these advanced platforms and the proper authoring software, excellent education and training courses emerge. Although we have yet to see the computer campus or school that has eliminated all teachers, these computer teaching systems are gaining in capability and popularity. Continued growth in the numbers of platforms and courses will be seen in the future as the systems get cheaper and authoring gets easier. It is conceivable that, within our lifetimes, many homes will have computer-based training systems that families use for assistance with school work, training for job skills, and courses for self-enrichment.

19

Optoelectronics

INTRODUCTION

Optoelectronics is the field in which we deal with both electronics and light. Think about a calculator, or a digital electronic watch. What you look at to see the numbers is optoelectronics. The numbers on a calculator are probably either LEDs or LCDs. If you can see them in the dark, they are LEDs, and, if you can't, they are probably LCDs. What do you think is the most common device that has electrical inputs and light outputs? If you thought of a light bulb, you are on the right track. The most common electronic device with the same characteristics is the television. We will talk more about devices later in this chapter, but we will begin with a discussion of optoelectronics itself.

Optoelectronics is, as its name suggests, a combination of optics and electronics, or light and electrons. Optoelectronic devices can be divided into four broad categories: those that have electronic inputs and light outputs; those that have light inputs and electronic outputs; those that transmit light; and specialized light sources. We will discuss each in the order presented.

ELECTRONIC INPUTS AND LIGHT OUTPUTS

These devices have wires going in but emit light as their output. The numbers on a calculator are examples of this type of device. The LED, or light-emitting diode, is a digital device that has a high and/or low (digital) voltage as input and emits light (or no light, based on the input) as output. LEDs are commonly red, but they do exist in other colors, and new colors are under development. When LEDs were first developed, they looked like very small light bulbs or like little diodes with windows in them. Currently, the most common form of the LED is the number readout. This is usually a 7- or 8-segment LED, which means it can show any number between 0 and 9. The only difference between the 7- and

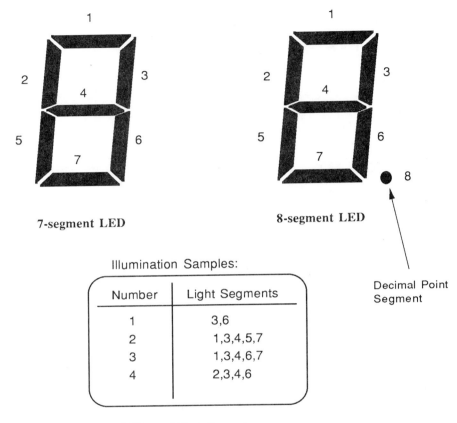

7-segment LED　　　　　　　　8-segment LED

Decimal Point
Segment

Illumination Samples:

Number	Light Segments
1	3,6
2	1,3,4,5,7
3	1,3,4,6,7
4	2,3,4,6

Figure 19-1　　Numeric LEDs and Their Layouts

8-segment devices is the addition of a decimal point to the 8-segment. Figure 19-1 shows the layouts for both 7- and 8-segment LEDs.

The 7- and 8-segment LEDs are fine for numbers, but what if you need letters as output? You have probably seen a 7-segment LED used for letters and know that it is not a very good solution. Figure 19-2 shows how some letters look when they are displayed using a 7-segment LED.

Another type of LED, called the matrix LED, solves this problem. The matrix LED has rows and columns of LEDs and any letter can be represented in upper or lower case by lighting up the proper segments. Figure 19-3 shows a matrix LED and some examples of combinations used for various letters.

The next, and newer, type of visible output device is the LCD, or liquid crystal display. This has a silvery or grayish look to it and is found in many of the newer calculators. The LCD requires much less current to

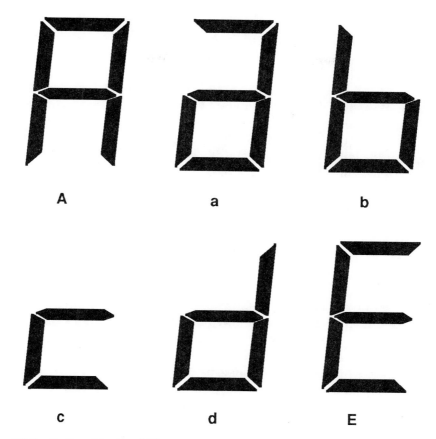

A   a   b

c   d   E

Figure 19-2   Letters Displayed Using 7-Segment LED

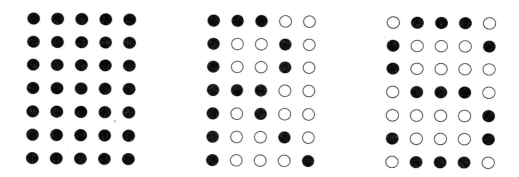

Figure 19-3   The Matrix LED and Some Examples

operate than the LED because it does not actually emit any light. The crystals in the liquid are normally transparent, but when a voltage is applied to them, they turn opaque, or nearly so. They become a very dark gray and this color is what we see when we look at the display. The major drawback of the LCD is that it cannot be used in the dark or even in dimly lit places. There are special low-light LCDs for use in low-light areas, but if an output is needed in relative darkness, the LED is the proper choice.

The TV picture tube is another device that has electronic inputs and light outputs. It operates in the following way. First, an electron gun shoots an electron stream at the back (inside) of the picture tube. The inside of the front of the tube is coated with a phosphor substance that emits light when struck by an electron beam. We control the intensity of the electron stream with the brightness control and the picture circuitry. The more intense the electron stream, the brighter the light emitted from the phosphor. The electron beam is directed to all parts of the screen in sequence by electromagnets called deflection coils. These coils bend the electron stream so that the beam, and the subsequent light, are kept in synchronization with the scanning taking place in the camera tube. The camera tube is an optoelectronic device also. As the camera tube looks at a specific place on its screen, the electron beam in the TV receiver is coordinated to stay in time so that the picture reproduced on your screen is just like the picture being scanned by the camera tube in the TV studio.

A video camcorder is another optoelectronics device. Some of the older camcorders have camera tubes in them for scanning the light images they are pointed at. These tubes were called vidicons. The newer camcorders have much more advanced image light sensors. If a camcorder's labeling says CCD image system or 3-chip image system, it is one that uses light-sensitive transistors or diodes to convert the light into electrical energy. These newer cameras are much more reliable and much less prone to damage than their predecessors.

To get color TV, sets of three dots of different color phosphors are arranged all over the back side of the screen. The three colors used are red, green, and blue. This is abbreviated RGB and you will see this acronym often in electronics and computer literature. The electron beam is directed at the proper color dot to provide the color light output. Some TVs have three separate electron guns, one for each of the three colors. Sony is the biggest user of the three-gun, or Trinitron, system and is recognized as a leader in color picture clarity, sharpness, and trueness. The picture tube has been with us for many years but developments on the horizon threaten the lifespan of the CRT.

One type of specialized light output device under development is the multicolor LED array, sometimes called the light wall or LED wall. This is the so-called TV of the future. Instead of having a picture tube, as we are used to seeing, we will look at an array or matrix of LEDs made up of red, blue, and green LEDs arranged in a sequential order. This arrangement is similar to that of the color TV picture tube, except that the dots of light are LEDs rather than glowing phosphors. These new devices are much lighter, more compact, and easier to maintain than the older CRTs. A new TV might be a large, picture-like screen that you hang on the wall wherever you like. It would be only a few inches thick and could be hung almost anywhere. These output devices could also be as large as desired. Although they sound fantastic, these new TVs will be in our homes sooner than you might think.

LIGHT INPUTS AND ELECTRONIC OUTPUTS

This second category of devices uses light as inputs and provides electronic signals or voltages as outputs. We briefly mentioned one such device in the previous section: the TV camera tube. Today, however, most of the devices that turn light into electrical energy are solid-state devices, such as diodes, transistors, FETs, triacs, and the like. We will now explore a few of these devices.

You learned in previous chapters that a transistor controls current flow and voltage by varying the bias voltages. For a phototransistor, this bias voltage is replaced by a light source. The conduction of the transistor is controlled by the amount of light received by the device. From what you know about diodes, you can figure out what happens. When a photodiode is in the dark, no current flows, but, if there is light, it very quickly conducts electricity. This rapid action is an important point as the photodiode has the fastest response time of all the photoactive devices.

As you might imagine, there are light-operated resistors. These are called photoconductive cells. Their resistance varies with the amount of light they receive. These devices are used in some circuits but they have several severe problems. They have a slow response time compared to the devices they are normally connected to. Second, they are unstable in conditions of varying temperature, so applications must be limited to constant temperature situations or the device must be protected from temperature changes.

Perhaps the light input devices we are most familiar with are the photovoltaic cells, or photocells. These are the small panels on a solar calculator that generate the power to run it. These tiny cells turn the light in a normal room into enough voltage and current to operate a calculator indefinitely. They are reliable and never need replacement as they will last as long as any of the other components in your electronic adding machine. Some people have solar cells mounted on their roofs to use the light of the sun to provide electricity or heat for their homes. In specialty catalogs, small lights for garden paths are a combination of photocells, rechargeable batteries, and lights. During the day, the photocell turns light into electricity and charges the battery. As darkness falls, the photocell shuts down and the battery provides the power to run the light. Over several hours, the battery will discharge and the light will go out, but the next day the cycle starts over again.

LASERS

A laser light has three characteristics that give it unique properties. Laser light is monochromatic, collimated, and coherent. Monochromatic means that the light is all one color or, stated in the terms of a physicist, all of one wavelength. Light is energy that is made up of several possible frequencies. Most light has many different frequencies in it. When you hold a prism or a piece of glass in a beam of light, it will show a rainbow-like set of colors. These colors represent the various light frequencies in the light shining through the prism. If you were to shine a laser through a prism, only one color would appear.

The second property of lasers is that they are collimated, or focused and straightened. This means that all of the light rays are parallel to each other. If you take a flashlight, shine it at a wall, and then move to different distances from the wall, the size of the circle of the beam of light will change. The light rays are not parallel to each other; they move apart as they leave the source. The farther you are from the wall, the bigger the circle. If you had a laser flashlight, this would not happen. The diameter of the circle would be the same whether you were two or two hundred feet from the wall. This is collimation.

The third feature of lasers is that they are coherent, a worthy goal for all of us. For light, this means that all of the light rays are not only the same frequency and headed in the same direction, but they are all in phase as well. Figure 19-4 illustrates the characteristics of laser light.

You now know the characteristics of laser light, but it might be useful also to know where the name laser came from. It is an acronym of the phrase "light amplification by stimulated emission of radiation." This

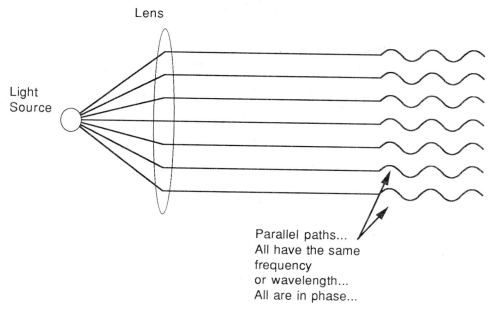

Figure 19-4   Laser Light Characteristics

partially explains why you must be careful around lasers. You should not look directly into laser light for any prolonged length of time or into any high-power laser at all. Exposure to laser light can be damaging to your eyes and to other body parts.

TRANSMISSION MEDIA

The last area of optoelectronics to be discussed here is transmission media. We know we can shoot a laser beam through the air, and this works adequately for some applications, but air bounces the light around and causes interference and attenuation (loss of signal strength). To use light for long ranges, we need a protected environment for the light to travel in. Fiber optics answers this need. Optical fibers are small (usually) glass or plastic solid rods that allow light to pass along their length with very little distortion or signal loss.

The development of the optical fiber has made the use of light for communications practical and popular. You have probably seen the commercials for long-distance telephone services advertising their use of fiber optics to improve the quality of their circuits. When used properly, fiber-optic transmission is better, cheaper, more reliable, and more secure than sending signals through the air or through wires. The energy used is light, instead of electromagnetic energy, and it has been developed for communications use to the point where it has surpassed the capability and usefulness of electronic communication systems. It is going to be years before we get rid of all of our wires and radio waves, but light is fast becoming the standard for communications systems for radio, TV, telephone, and data communications.

Fiber cables are small, cheap, reliable, and getting easier to work with. The two main advantages of fiber cables over metallic wires are the speed of transmission possible and the better transmission performance, that is, less signal distortion and attenuation. It is possible that within a few years all of our phone calls will use some optical devices in the connection.

This brings up one last point. To get from electronics to light and back again, we need some special devices to transform the energy into the form we need. These devices are called optocouplers. There are a variety of optocouplers, depending on their particular purpose and the circuits they will be used in, but all of them convert light energy into electrical energy, or vice versa. The speed at which this is done is critical to the efficiency of the circuits they are connected in and much development is taking place in this field.

Epilogue

We honestly did not know how to end this book. Obviously, there is much more to learn about electricity and electronics than we have presented, but our purpose here is to introduce the reader to the basics and provide some insight into how pervasive the impact of electronics is on our lives. A person living in any industrialized country is affected or served by applications of electricity every day. From the digital alarm clocks that wake us in the morning to the controls that operate our heaters so we can sleep comfortably at night, we are touched by electronics. Our work, our communications, our business world, and many of the games we play and watch depend on our controlled use of the tiny electron.

This book can be used effectively as an introductory text by students majoring in technical topics, but it is intended for use by students in non-technical fields. There are many intelligent people who are interested in, and at times frustrated by, their lack of understanding of electricity. This book was written to demystify this invisible force. Unless some great unforeseen changes drastically modify the course of the modern world, we can expect to see research and applications in electronics continue to increase. Electronics will continue to play an ever-increasing part in our lives and in society and there is little we can do to stop it. From this perspective, it makes sense for all of us to know something about the field.

As is true of much technology, it can be both a curse and a blessing — the disease and the medicine. As you read this, there is no doubt someone working on some type of weapon system that uses electronics as its control system. Hopefully, there is also research underway that will help us live healthier, happier, and more productive lives as individuals, cultures, and as members of the earth society. Electronics is but a tool in the hands of craftsmen. It must be fashioned responsibly into applications that make our lives better.

As innovation continues at an unprecedented rate, we will no doubt see bigger and better televisions, higher-tech and better sound equipment, better and more feature-laden communications systems, better transportation systems and vehicles, safer homes, smaller and more capable computers, new health-care equipment, and, in general, spend more time interacting with electronic equipment. We will continue to see our lives changed by developments in technology. The more informed we are about the things that shape our lives, the better prepared we are to make informed judgments about what is good and what is bad. This is perhaps the underlying purpose of this book — to present to the non-technical person information that we all need to fulfill our responsibilities as citizens. This sounds pretty serious, and it is. We have all been curious at one time or another about why some light bulbs are brighter than others and why, at Christmas, when one goes out, the rest stay lit. Hopefully, we have provided the reader with a greater understanding of the world around us and provided the necessary information to help readers make intelligent decisions.

Index